Behind Chained Gates

Moira Linaker

HAYLOFT

First published March 2004

Second Edition April 2004

Hayloft Publishing Ltd, Kirkby Stephen,
Cumbria, CA17 4EU.

tel: (017683) 42300
fax. (017683) 41568
e-mail: dawn@hayloft.org.uk
web: www.hayloft.org.uk

ISBN 1 904524 168

A catalogue record for this book is available
from the British Library

Cover photograph courtesy of PA Photos/Owen Humphreys

Produced, printed and bound in Great Britain

CONTENTS

This book is dedicated to the memory of my son, Stephen, whose spirit gave me strength when I needed it most.

FOREWORD

Had it not been for the outbreak of Britain's disastrous epidemic of foot and mouth disease in 2001, it is unlikely that the literary world would have heard of Moira Linaker - the 'Rottweiler'.

It wasn't until 1996 that she became a smallholder - as she says herself, more by accident than design - and having previously owned two dogs and assorted cats went out to buy a couple of sheep to help keep the grass under control on her recently acquired one acre of land.

The fact that she came home with a small flock, because she couldn't face the thought of them being slaughtered as merely surplus to requirements tells the reader much about this remarkable woman. Tiny - less than five feet tall - she put the 'good life' into practice on her Cumbrian smallholding, with the help of friends. No stranger to the kind of personal tragedy that would have laid most of us low, the daily care of her ever-increasing collection of animals carried her through - until 'foot and mouth' arrived in Cumbria in the early spring of 2001.

We all know what happened then... I was given the task of daily broadcasts to Cumbria, one of the worst affected regions of Britain, and quickly became aware of the devastation this disease wrought among the farming community and those who depend on it. We heard tales of intimidation, coercion and bullying of farmers who tried to resist the 3km culling of healthy animals. Moira Linaker refused to be bullied, resisted, and won - and her remarkable book tells you how, from somewhere, she got the strength and determination to do so - becoming the scourge of the Ministry of Agriculture, Fisheries and Food - MAFF - later DEFRA - and earning from them the nickname 'the Rottweiler'.

What *Behind Chained Gates* tells, though, is not just the story of one woman's protest at what she saw as heavy handed and ill-informed bureaucracy, not just the fight against an unseen and deadly opponent - it also tells a very human story of an ordinary woman dealing with a life-time of extraordinary events. It's told with a great humour, and a total absence of self regard - the same qualities that gained international attention and recognition, and Royal approval. Above all, this book is written from the heart - I hope it will be read by millions.

Anne Hopper, Broadcaster.

1

THE COTTAGE

I moved to Cumbria from Newcastle upon Tyne in 1996 and found an almost derelict cottage with an acre of land at Warwick Bridge, four miles from Carlisle. Overlooked by nothing but fields and trees, the bedroom window gave a spectacular panoramic view of the river Eden which I could imagine changing with the seasons from lush greens in summer to rustic reds in autumn. Yet I was only minutes from the main road and two miles from the M6.

The cottage had not been lived in for over nine years and it showed. However, I just knew it had potential, while realising that a lot of hard work was in store both inside and out to achieve this. I had been used to restoring past houses that I had lived in, but this time I was on my own apart from my two dogs: Chloe, a standard Dachshund, and Holly, a Doberman crossed with a Rhodesian Ridgeback.

That first Christmas Eve in the cottage is one that I will never forget. The only thing that was nice about Christmas that year was the open coal fire, which Chloe, Holly and I fought to be in front of, both dogs thinking this great fun since neither had been used to a real fire. Getting used to no outside street lights and to the strange noises at night was daunting, but it was a comfort to see the distant lights on the main road and in time the hooting of owls and screeching of bats lost their power to shock. And during the day I could watch the oyster catchers flying across the river and breathe in the wonderful silence that only the country can provide.

For the first two months, the dogs and I slept downstairs. Chloe slept with me on a sofa, while Holly stretched out in front of the coal fire. Holly would have liked to have been on the sofa too but, so far as Chloe was concerned, possession was most definitely nine tenths of the law and a determined Dachshund in situ is not to be trifled with, as more than one visitor to the cottage has found out.

The priority was to decorate a bedroom and, when it was finished, I dragged myself upstairs and collapsed into bed. Unfortunately, Chloe decided that she should accompany me and crawled under the duvet. Not to be left out, Holly came upstairs too, only to be sharply rebuffed by Chloe and beat a retreat downstairs to the sofa, which of course was now vacant for occupation. Eventually, they settled into a 'Cox and Box' arrangement. Chloe slept in the bed with me during the night and, in the morning, when we had both come downstairs, Holly would slope up to the bedroom and take up residence for the day.

I decorated non stop all winter, one room after another, so as to be finished by the time it was spring and be able to start on the outside. Facing me was nine years growth of weeds, some of which were at least ten foot high. Since I am only five foot nothing, clearing these was going to be quite a task and I realised after a week that I was not getting very far and needed some help. I found a chap who had a tractor and he agreed to come and clear the lot for me. It took him a week to clear the land, during which a fire burnt constantly to get rid of the weeds.

When that was done, another man came to plough the land and, once that had been levelled, I bought bags of grass seed and spread the seed as evenly as possible by hand. Then I bought some fencing and divided the land into two paddocks, separated by a path from the cottage to the road, while planting trees around my boundary.

Everything was starting to take shape and by early summer the grass was growing, the fences had been painted and the trees had all taken. I was pleased with the results of my efforts and people would stop as they walked past the cottage and congratulate me on how nice everything was looking.

I now had an acre of grass to look after and, since I did not already possess a conventional lawn mower, I decided that perhaps it would be nicer to get an 'animal lawn mower' instead. I had noticed that the local radio, BBC Radio Cumbria, had a daily slot at noon, called the 'Lamb Bank', advertising day old lambs for sale, usually from ewes which had given birth to three lambs. I learnt that farmers have this notion that ewes can only cope with feeding two lambs and therefore a third lamb will end up not being fed, as the other two will have consumed all of her milk. (In fact, I have since found that some ewes can be quite capable of producing enough milk to feed three lambs). So, having borrowed a horsebox for use as a shed and filled it with straw, I made arrangements to go and look at the day old lambs at a nearby farm.

When I got there, it was rather like visiting the local animal refuge.

There were fifteen lambs inside metal drums, with a heat lamp above to keep them warm, and, as one approached, the noise became deafening, because they had already learnt to associate the presence of humans with food. It was heart breaking to see the tiny things with no mother to care for them. I asked how much they were and the farmer said £5 each.

My next (foolish) question was to ask what would happen if no one wanted them. 'In that case, we will knock them on the head,' came the reply. That was it. I bought all fifteen on the spot. The farmer put them inside paper sacks and into the boot of my little Honda Civic and I was off.

On the way home, I stopped at an agricultural shop and bought a large bag of lamb milk and fifteen feeding bottles with teats. Once I had managed to carry the lambs out of my car and safely install them inside the horsebox, I proceeded to mix fifteen bottles of milk and carry these out in a basket, along with a box of tissues.

What a sight and sound greeted me. It was like looking into a bird's nest with all of them wanting to be fed at the same time, except that I do not think there are any birds which return to their nests to find as many as fifteen expectant mouths waiting for them. I sat on a bale of straw, a bottle of milk in each hand and one between my knees so that I could at least manage three in one go. Needless to say the remaining twelve were going crazy, jumping on the ones being fed and crawling all over me.

Eventually I had fifteen empty bottles but I was far from certain that I had fifteen full lambs, because it was difficult to tell them apart and some were still crying for more. I could not be sure whether these were ones who had missed out or who were simply greedy.

Four hours later, I had to begin all over again and every four hours after that, not only during the day but also during the night, which was worse because I had no outside lights to show me what I was doing. I had to hold a torch between my knees, which meant that I could only feed two lambs at a time instead of three and, as a result, night feeding took longer. At least I was now able to distinguish the lambs from each other so that I knew that no one was missing out on the milk.

I continued with this performance for about three weeks until I heard about and acquired a lamb bucket (or lamb bar). This was a large container, which could hold up to eight bottles - two pushed through each side, like cannons through the portholes of a warship - so enabling eight lambs to be fed at once. After their individual attention, the lambs took some time getting used to the fact that 'Mum' had now become a bottle at the end of a bucket in place of a bottle at the end of a hand or a knee. But eventually they all got the message that it was this or nothing and stopped trying to suck my fingers and nuzzle my legs.

After a few weeks the weather was warm enough for them to play out-side and it was a delight to see them skipping about. I could and did watch them for hours. At dusk they would have a mad half hour and play chase with each other, before I shut them up in the horsebox for the night. After a while, I noticed that the lambs would settle down in the same lit-tle gangs that had played together during the day. This was my first real-isation that sheep had individual personalities and would make friends with some but not others.

One day I was busy mucking out the horsebox when a car pulled onto my drive. The car was in dire need of a good wash and polish and judg-ing from its state it could only belong to a farmer. I walked over to the gate because visitors generally do not dare to come further than this once they have spotted Holly wandering around. She looks very much the watchdog, aided and abetted by her loud bark and a large notice dis-played on the gate, which reads 'KEEP OUT - DOBERMAN ON GUARD'. This is a bit of a giggle, because actually I have never known her hurt anybody. The one you have to watch is Chloe who, given the chance, will go for any ankle within range. I am ashamed to admit that she can count among her 'hits' the vicar's wife, a local councillor and the Mayor of Carlisle.

A man had got out of the car as I approached the gate. 'Afternoon,' he said, 'I am told that you like sheep.' I was puzzled at this remark but before I could answer he continued, 'I breed pedigree Leicesters and one ewe's dropped a black one.'

I presumed he meant that the ewe had given birth to a black lamb. 'Did she?' I said, wondering what on earth that had to do with me.

'Well, I removed it from her and left her with its white sister.'

Was he a racist I thought to myself? 'Well, the butcher doesn't like black lambs because the meat's too dark.'

'Oh,' was all I could think to say, still wondering what this had to do with me.

'Well, would you like to have it?' With that, he went back to his car and brought out a sack. When he had returned to the gate he opened the sack and I was met by two big eyes. 'She is used to dogs,' he said, looking at both of mine. 'She has been sleeping with the collie at night in the shed. And she's used to bottle,' (by which I knew he meant she was a pet lamb brought up on a bottle of milk). 'She's three weeks old and I've called her Topsy, because that's how she's growing. Trouble is she thinks she's a dog and keeps wanting to go in doors with the collie and my daughter's none too pleased about that and says she has to go.'

While he was talking, I was still looking at those eyes in the sack. It was just like looking into a deep millpond.

The farmer continued, 'If you don't want her, I will have to knock her on the head.'

Oh no, I thought, not again. Had word got round the farming community that there was this soft woman in Cumbria who would take any lamb you wanted to off-load if you spun her this line?

'Yes,' I heard a voice say, 'I will have her.'

And that was how I acquired my first pedigree sheep, a Blue Faced Leicester, although you could hardly describe Topsy as a beauty, with her prominent Roman nose and spindly legs.

She soon settled in and made friends with the other lambs who were quite intrigued with this black thing and kept having a sniff just to make sure that she really was a sheep

Topsy was well named and she 'growed and growed' just as her namesake in the story of *Uncle Tom's Cabin*. She was soon head and shoulders above the other sheep and they began to follow her everywhere. The only problem was that Topsy could work anything out. Sheep don't have brains? Don't you believe it!

By now, I had cultivated a small but well planted garden at the back of the cottage. It was in full bloom with rose trees and annuals and it looked a picture. A wrought iron gate separated the sheep paddock from both the garden and the cottage.

One day, I went out shopping and on my return I was met at the gate to the main drive by Topsy followed by some of the others. Now, in order to get to the main drive gate, there was no alternative but to go through the garden. Except that now, there was no garden to speak of. All that remained were stalks, where two hours earlier there had been flowers.

They had even eaten my sweet peas that were planted in two pots and which had made a lovely arch.

It was unbelievable that so few sheep could have done so much damage in such a short time. I began to think that there was something in the 'knocking them on the head' approach after all.

So, there was nothing for it but to start ensuring that gates were tied up. At first, I just did this with bows until a further experience of Topsy's initiative proved that something stronger was required.

One morning, when I was busy upstairs in the cottage, I heard a noise in the kitchen and realised it was neither of the dogs. Sure enough, it was Topsy paying a visit. Thank goodness she did not arrive upstairs as I dread to think of the mess she would have made. Bows on the gates were abandoned in favour of double knots.

Despite these and other experiences, Topsy and I became firm friends. She grew to become almost as tall as me and seemed to understand every word I said to her. As soon as I entered the paddock, her big Roman nose would go straight into my pocket in search of the biscuits she knew would be inside. I was forever repairing torn pockets on my coats.

Topsy was a natural flock leader. If I wanted other sheep to come to me or go anywhere, I just needed to call Topsy to round them up and she would do the rest. With her around I did not need a sheepdog.

2

The Good Life?

The fifteen lambs began to grow and I knew I only had space for about four sheep and that the rest would have to go. Fortunately I found a couple who had a smallholding and who were looking for some breeding stock. They offered to buy all of them and, much to my relief, because they were all gimmers (which I had now learnt was what you called girl sheep) none had to go for slaughter. They settled in well at their new home and I would often visit them and find that they always remembered me. As I have said already, sheep have brains.

With the departure of what could truly be called the First Fifteen, all I had left was Topsy who I could not bear to part with, as she was such a character. So, when I saw a rare breed sale advertised in the local paper, I decided to go and see if I could buy a couple of goats to keep the grass down and to keep Topsy company. I reasoned that as Topsy looked more like a goat than a sheep she would look less out of place with two goats.

I had never been to a rare breed sale before and was quite unprepared for the variety of animals on show. However, among all the many different pens, there was one area to which I kept being drawn back and it was not one occupied by goats.

What had caught my eye was a group of sheep that I can only describe as looking like woolly teddy bears - and when I say woolly do I mean woolly. The wool went right down to each hoof and completely covered the face so that it seemed as if the sheep would not be able to see out, rather like a guardsman with a bearskin.

These sheep I discovered were called Ryelands.

I spoke to some of the owners who were delighted to tell me how docile they were and what an ideal sheep for a beginner. Because of their short legs it was difficult for them to jump out of a field and, if they did happen to get out, they rarely went further than the next welcoming patch of grass, so that you did not have to run too far to catch them.

I went into the auction and was soon raising my hand to bid. I bought four ewe lambs and once again the boot of my Honda Civic was transporting sheep back to the cottage.

Thankfully this time I did not have to bottle feed. The Ryelands settled into the paddocks and it did not take long for them to come to me when called, with the added enticement of a digestive biscuit or two. I gave each of them a name and in no time at all they responded individually to Katie, Ellie and - more impressively - Athene and Andromeda.

Not long after the rare breed sale, I happened to pass the local auction mart and thought I would go to see what went on there. A sheep sale was in progress but the first thing I noticed was that the audience was almost entirely male, because there was only one other woman at the ringside apart from me. The men stood by, resting their chins on sticks and deep in conversation. I was convinced that most of them were there just to get away from the farm (or the wife) for the morning and catch up on the local gossip, since no one seemed to be bidding. But in fact the auctioneer knew who wanted what by the slightest of gestures - the tilt of a head or the raising of a shoulder. I could feel my nose itching but was too scared to scratch in case my action was misinterpreted as a bid.

Suddenly into the ring came one ewe all on her own. She had a Roman nose just like Topsy's, so I knew she must be a Leicester, and ordinarily that would have been the most noticeable thing about her, except that this ewe had hardly any wool on her back. Indeed, apart from odd patches, she was about as naked a sheep as could be imagined. She trotted round the ring, looking at everyone and with her ears straight up in the air, a sure sign that she was nervous of her surroundings.

Two farmers standing next to me were laughing at this poor animal and I heard one of them say to the other, 'I bet he buys that one,' nodding towards a local restaurateur nearby, who was showing signs of keen interest.

'Aye,' said his friend, 'That'll be on the kebab spit tomorrow.'

Oh no it won't, I said to myself as the bidding started.

'Who will give me two pounds?' asked the auctioneer.

The kebab man put up his hand and so did I, giving him my best Paddington Bear stare at the same time.

'Am I bid four pounds?' asked the auctioneer.

'Five!' I yelled, as I put up my hand.

What had I done? The kebab man looked at me in disbelief, shrugged his shoulders and walked away.

A farmer I knew from the next village came over to me and asked me what on earth I wanted with 'that thing'. I was too embarrassed to tell him the truth but he kindly offered to bring her home for me. I got out as soon as I could and paid my five pounds plus another one pound fifty in tax.

Fiver was duly delivered and, when my friend let her out of his trailer, she came up to me and, as if to say thank you, rubbed her big nose on my arm.

Once let loose in the field behind the cottage, she galloped around, kicking up her back legs just like a horse. Eventually she spotted Topsy, who was standing in the field watching this performance, and ran over to her. Topsy gently pushed her away and I could almost hear her say to the newcomer, 'This is my patch, I'm the boss and don't you forget it.'

Judging by her teeth, which I checked the next day, Fiver was only a yearling and it was obvious that she had been brought up by her previous owner as a pet lamb, because she instinctively trusted everyone that she met. In time Fiver and Topsy became good friends, but it was always clear that Topsy was the dominant one in their relationship.

Having said that, when it came to feeding time Fiver could eat twice as fast as Topsy or any of the other sheep. She was easily the greediest animal of any description that I have ever encountered and none too fussy about what she ate.

On one occasion her greed threatened to have dire consequences. I had been out and returned to find that the gate to the field was open. All the sheep appeared to be at the far end of the field until I realised that Fiver was not among them. I found her lying in the shed, frothing at the mouth and blown up like a balloon.

I went back to my drive and discovered that a bush of Forest Flame had been chewed to its stalks. I ran indoors and looked up this bush in one of my gardening books. It was part of the Rhododendron family and deadly poisonous to sheep. I called out the vet. He gave Fiver an injection and gave me some powder to mix with water, before administering to her mouth with a syringe so as to counter dehydration. He did not hold out much hope.

I rigged up a heat lamp in the shed and gave her a soft blanket, because she was shivering. The vet said to leave her until the morning. He did not say what time in the morning and when it had got to four o'clock I decided I could not wait any longer. I had to go and check on her.

Long before I reached the shed, I could hear an unmistakably deep blare, and when I got to the door, there she was, standing up as if nothing had been wrong with her. I stood the blaring as long as I could before giving her some food. The vet called in a few hours later on his way to the surgery and could not believe his eyes when he saw her. The fact that she had survived this experience convinced me that Fiver must have been crossed with a goat.

Several times afterwards she pigged out on her food and went down with a bloated stomach. Each time I would have to get another supply of the powder, which the vet had given me on that first occasion, and make her drink litres of this orange looking liquid in order to get rid of the wind.

Apart from her eating habits, the other problem with Fiver was that her wool never grew. I tried just about everything including homeopathic products but nothing worked. I even had some of her wool sent away for analysis. She was perfectly healthy but just had little or no wool.

More than one passer by thought Fiver was a llama. This was in spite of her skin being more like that of an elephant. I bought regular supplies of oil from the chemist to keep her skin supple and even tried her with some cream that is more commonly used to prevent bed sores for bedridden geriatrics.

In the end I had to make her a cotton coat from a man's shirt so as to keep the sun off her back in the summer, otherwise she would have got sun burn, and another coat to keep her warm in the winter. She detested the rain and I would always find her clamouring to be let inside my shed as soon as any started to fall.

About the same time as getting Fiver, I also acquired some small brown hens and a Toulouse goose called Jemima. I was beginning to feel like Felicity Kendal's character, Barbara, from *The Good Life*. I remember watching that on TV and wishing that I could be like that and here I now was spending every daylight hour outside with my animals and finding it so rewarding - and, of course, I did not have to put up with anyone like Penelope Keith's Margo for a next door neighbour!

Jemima had been brought up with hens and understandably thought she was one. She happily mixed with the brown hens and slept with them at night. As I intended to get some other geese, I thought I had better begin to re-educate her, particularly so far as water was concerned. I started with a washing up bowl and Jemima would gingerly put one foot in the water and waddle round the edge of the bowl while keeping the other foot on the grass. After a while, she felt sufficiently certain to go in with both feet and in no time had graduated to a baby bath and finally a paddling pool.

It was at this point that she was joined by a gander and two other geese. Any fears that Jemima might think she was still a hen and not realise her true vocation soon vanished. The hens were history and Jemima had a new gang to hang out with. She and the other geese splashed happily in and out of the paddling pool, until one day the gander got over excited and punctured it. I bought another paddling pool but that did not last long either and I realised there was nothing for it but to try and make them a pond.

Because the land was on riverbed soil, it was far too hard for me to dig manually and so I hired a mini mechanical digger to do the job. 'Any fool can use this', said the man who delivered it to the cottage. Well, not this one.

I carefully marked out the area that I wanted to turn into a pond and started the digger. It did not appear to have anything approximating to a steering wheel and in no time at all had taken me across the paddock, out of my designated pond zone and into the hedge. Having regained a semblance of control, it then decided to nose dive into the ground as if it were in a race to get to the centre of the Earth. With an almighty struggle I pulled it out, adjusted the settings and then went round and round in circles. The digger resisted all my attempts to go where I wanted it to go and do what I wanted it to do. Now, I do not give up easily but, having wrecked half the paddock and with no sign of a pond emerging from my efforts, I gave up on this.

The next day when the man came back to reclaim his digger, he surveyed the wreckage, took pity on me and did the job himself. It took him all of ten minutes and he did not charge me a penny.

I lined out the hole made by the digger, filled it with water and the geese had their pond. One might say that all was going swimmingly and so it was, until the geese began to lay eggs, whereupon the gander underwent a complete change of personality.

He was an Emden, which are the largest of the white geese, and I realised he was just being a gentleman and protective towards the ladies. But there was nothing gentlemanly in his behaviour towards me. A gander, someone told me, is also called a steg in Cumbria and indeed in other parts of northern England. I could think of a few other names to call this particular steg and none of them were printable.

I had to creep across the paddock to try and collect the eggs and each time I was spotted and each time it was a case of him or me. I had to arm myself with a big stick to beat him off. I was terrified of him and he knew it. He would screech obscenities at me and I would yell them back at him (most unlike Felicity Kendal). Then he would put his head down and start towards me and I would run as fast as I could to the safety of the paddock gate.

At night I had a repeat performance when it was time to shut the geese up in their shed for safety from any foxes. I would don an old pink ski suit, grab my stick and with an old shoe rack for a riot shield march out to do battle. On at least two occasions the gander flew up towards my face and each time I managed to grab him by the neck and literally rolled over on the grass before getting him inside the goose shed.

Word must have got round about this daily spectacle because I noticed that dog owners seemed to be timing their walks past the cottage to coincide with geese shutting up time. Little groups of spectators would congregate in the road waiting patiently for me to emerge into the ring.

'Go on lass. Let him see who's boss!' I would hear from the roadside, followed by an ironic burst of applause when I had finally succeeded in getting the gander and his harem into their shed for the night. I would retreat to the cottage muttering under my breath about it being all right for some.

Eventually I got sick of providing free spectator sport and started to wait until dark before shutting up the geese. Not only did this put a stop to my unwanted audience but it also had an effect on the gander because I discovered that he did not like the light from my torch being shone at him, although I still had to go out with the stick and the shoe rack as well. I remember thinking that perhaps Luke Skywalker's light sabre would have been the ideal weapon for subduing the gander.

In retrospect I am amazed that I tolerated the gander as long as I did.

When the geese were out of season, he would calm down and behave quite reasonably and I suppose one tended to forget and forgive until the next time came round. Finally, I had to find him a new home and let him go with his favourite goose, also an Emden, with whom I hear he still lives happily and, I might add, with a man to master him.

I was left with the other two geese: Jemima and Eric. Yes, I know Eric is a boy's name but her previous owner had already christened her Eric, after the footballer Eric Cantona, before realising that Eric was not a gander. So, although it would have been easy to change the name to Erica, somehow Eric seemed to fit. In the absence of the gander, neither Jemima nor Eric was any trouble at all and I was able to put away my stick and shoe rack.

What I did have trouble with were my small brown hens. These had now grown and I noticed kept flying up into the trees, so that when it came to shut them up for the night and keep them safe from foxes it was quite a job to get them down.

It was only after a while that I found out that what I thought were ordinary brown hens were in fact Indian game birds, which explained their readiness to take to the air. I decided to part company with these before they parted company with me. I replaced them with some Light Sussex hens, which I bought from someone I met at another rare breed sale. Light Sussex are one of the oldest breeds of hens and because of their weight you do not have to worry about them flying off. I am told that they are not uncommon in the south of England but in the north you tend to find them only at rare breed sales. At any rate, the Light Sussex proved to be no problem and hens, geese and sheep co-existed quite happily, although not always peacefully.

Around this time I encountered another rare breed. Only this one was human. The Light Sussex hens proved to be good layers of eggs and I was also growing an abundance of tomatoes in a lean-to that I had put up at one side of the cottage, which attracted more than its fair share of sun. I am not a great eater of eggs and there were far more tomatoes than I could consume. So I decided to put up a sign advertising eggs and tomatoes for sale.

One afternoon I was inside the cottage but Holly and Chloe were both outside. I heard them start barking and carry on barking. So I realised that I must have a visitor. I looked out from the kitchen. A small black car had parked opposite the little gate at the end of my path and a woman had got out. As I came to the front door, I could see her standing at the gate and could hear her addressing the two dogs, while they continued to bark.

'Now, we'll have no more of this carry on,' said my visitor in a no nonsense tone of voice, 'That's quite enough. Stop barking you two. I'm coming in.'

To my amazement, the dogs took notice. My goodness, I thought, Barbara Woodhouse has been re-incarnated, except that my visitor was quite a bit shorter than the famous dog trainer whose television programmes I had so much enjoyed years ago. She was wearing a green Barbour jacket and a green, wide brimmed, waxed hat, sporting Countryside Alliance and British Legion badges

'Good afternoon,' said my visitor and gestured towards the dogs, 'You have to show them who's boss.' I sighed silently at yet another Cumbrian telling me how to handle animals. 'Have you any tomatoes to spare, please? I would like to buy a couple of pounds. I trust you sell them in pounds. I am not having anything to do with kilos and all that European rubbish. I am going to make some tomato soup on my Aga.'

I invited her in while I went to get the tomatoes and asked if she would also like half a dozen eggs.

'No need, thank you very much,' she replied, 'I have hens of my own, you see. By the way, I am Susan Bull. I live just up the road at Great Corby. You must come and visit and see my bantams and my guinea fowl.'

It transpired that, in addition to hens, Susan also had ducks, of which her favourites were Mrs Frizell and Mrs Tea Cosy, a terrier called Huntley - there had been another called Palmer but the two of them had been too much of a handful so he had had to go - and two cats called Tabitha and PJ.

Susan was a retired district nurse and although she did not originate from Cumbria she had lived in the county for some thirty years. She had moved here when her late husband had retired from the RAF to become the signalman for the railway crossing at Great Corby.

The tomatoes were a great success and Susan would stop by once a week to replenish her supplies. We became good friends, as did Huntley, her terrier, with Chloe my dachshund. I think Chloe appreciated having a companion who was much nearer her own size than Holly was. But it may just have been the realisation that a visit from Huntley meant extra biscuits for her. Susan, for her part, took to calling Chloe and Holly, 'Cloak and Dagger'.

In time, Susan was to prove the staunchest of allies in circumstances that neither of us could have foreseen when we first met.

3

MR UNIVERSE

In the late summer I saw that the Cumberland Agricultural Show was taking place and, as I had never attended one before, decided I would go. Naturally I made for the sheep section where I came across the pens with Ryeland sheep. I had been thinking about getting a ram to go with my Ryeland ewes.

The owners were all busy brushing and trimming their sheep ready for judging of the various classes. In one pen at which I stopped a particular Ryeland ram caught my eye. He was very friendly and came up to me. What a beauty, I thought. His owner was busy putting on her white coat ready to go into the ring with one of her other sheep. I asked her various questions about the ram. She was very helpful and told me he was called Mr Universe and that he was a yearling. Then she had to go into the show ring with one of her sheep.

I just stood and looked at Mr Universe and he just stood and looked at me. He had great big soft eyes and I was smitten.

When his owner, Susan Bryden, had come back from the ring and was waiting for another class to be called, I asked her if he was for sale. Much to my delight she said he was but that she could not let him go until after the shows were finished for that year, since he was already booked in for appearances. Susan and her father lived across the Scottish border near Lockerbie and had bred prize winning Ryelands for a number of years.

We agreed a price and then it was Mr Universe's turn to enter the ring for shearling rams (another name for a year old sheep). He won first prize and continued to win reserve champion, beaten only by his father. It was easy to see where he got his good points from because his father was also a beauty. However, one thing that Mr Universe had that his father did not was an extra rib, with the result that he was unusually long.

I returned home and waited for the rest of the shows to finish, keeping a close eye on the newspapers for show results over the following weeks.

At last the day came when Susan Bryden and her father drove down from Lockerbie to deliver Mr Universe to the cottage. He walked out of the trailer looking even bigger than when I had last seen him earlier that year. I knew then that I had picked a star but little did I know then that he would become one of the most photographed of sheep and would appear in newspapers all over the world.

Once he spotted the girls he gave all of them the once over and looked at us, as if to say, 'Yes they will do very nicely, thank you,' and began eating grass. He settled in at once. Susan told me that he liked a cuddle and a piece of bread each morning and so he did, only soon the bread was substituted by a digestive biscuit.

By early October, Mr Universe had all my ewes in lamb. At least, I assumed he had, judging by all the red backs on show and bearing in mind that this was the colour that I had painted underneath him.

I booked myself into a lambing course at Newton Rigg Agricultural College in November and found this most helpful. I was taught how to stomach tube feed a weak and at risk lamb, but it was a bit off putting when they produced a dead lamb and I declined to try and slide the tube down the poor thing's throat. But I did watch very carefully and have managed to perform this exercise since on several occasions with great success.

We then had a break for lunch and I noticed that the fog was coming down thick and fast. Since I had to travel some twenty miles along the M6 I decided that I could not hang on for the important bit of how to lamb a ewe, which was a great pity.

February soon arrived and since, because of my inexperience, I was not absolutely sure when each ewe would lamb, I gave myself several sleepless nights unnecessarily.

By now I had had a shed built and my ewes were kept inside this once it became dark. Typically my nights would begin at ten o'clock, when I would make sure that all was well with the ewes. I would check them again at midnight and then set my alarm for a further call at 3am. Any aspiring burglar or passing insomniac would have had the shock of his life if his visit had coincided with one of my 3am ward rounds.

First out of the cottage came me, wearing my trusty old pink ski suit over my pyjamas and armed with a flash light, followed close at heel by Chloe the dachshund, followed by Holly the doberman cross breed and

23

bringing up the rear Tabitha the cat, the latest addition to the household after I had seen a mouse run across the kitchen floor.

After three weeks of this nightly performance, Chloe decided that I was quite mad, that she had had quite enough of this pantomime and that she was going to remain in bed, thank you very much. But Holly and Tabitha were made of sterner stuff and continued to escort me on my patrols. Even so, I used to pray for a full moon each night to light up my path to the shed.

Inside the shed itself I kept a low light on permanently at night and an old radio tuned into Classic FM. The idea of keeping a light on all the time was so that, on arriving in the shed, I would not unsettle the sheep by suddenly switching on a light or indeed by suddenly switching a light off when leaving. As for the classical music, it did seem to have a soothing effect. I wondered what Mark Griffiths and the other night time DJs would have said if they had known that their audience included a flock of expectant ewes. I did think of sending in a request for *Sheep May Safely Graze*.

Towards the end of February, during one of my midnight checks I noticed that one of the ewes was sitting alone in a corner and that she had been scratching the straw into a makeshift nest. This was a sure sign that something was about to happen, so I moved her into a pen of her own and left her to settle. I returned indoors, made a cup of tea, lit a cigarette and consulted my books on lambing.

One hour later I returned to the shed, with a somewhat confused Holly in tow, wondering why she was being called out earlier than usual. The ewe was very restless but there was nothing constructive that I could do to help her, so I came back to the cottage, made another cup of tea, lit another cigarette and consulted my lambing books again.

I returned for my regular 3am visit, with an even more confused Holly in tow. The ewe was still restless but nothing had happened, so I came back to the cottage, made yet another cup of tea, lit yet another cigarette but gave up on the lambing books in favour of an old copy of *Hello*. Pregnant sheep, I mused, are just like pregnant women. They too have various stages of labour to go through.

At 5am I decided to venture out again, this time on my own, because Holly had decided that Chloe had been right all along and that she would follow her example and stay indoors.

I put my head round the door of the shed and was met with the most wonderful sight. A beautiful white lamb stood drinking milk from his proud mother, who was washing and talking to her baby. After all those trips, I had missed out on the actual moment of birth. I told mum what a good girl she was, gave her some food, removed the afterbirth, sprayed the lamb's navel with antibiotic and left them both to bond. I returned to the cottage for a couple of hours sleep before the start of another day.

I had a brainwave to save having to make so many nightly trips out into the cold. Why not set up a baby alarm in my bedroom and connect it to the sheep shed? Then I would hear if any ewe sounded in distress and I could rush out to see her and, with a bit of luck, be in at the birth of a new lamb. In theory it sounded a great idea, so off I went the next day and bought a baby alarm, which I set up next to my bed and connected to the sheep shed.

What sounded great in theory was not so great in practice. At the slightest noise in the shed Chloe's head would surface from under the duvet. She would leap off the bed towards the alarm and bark her head off, which in turn would set off Holly barking downstairs. I had not realised just how much sheep chat to each other during the night until my baby alarm gave the game away.

I soon reverted to my nightly patrols but it was not long before I had witnessed my first birth of a lamb, and then a second and a third. Each was a wonderful experience but what impressed me particularly was how well the new mothers cared for their lambs and how in no time each lamb would recognise his or her own mother's voice as distinct from the others.

Topsy gave birth to two white Ryeland cross lambs, both with big black eyes and little Roman noses. Fiver went one better and had three lambs, all with big ears. Both were excellent mothers and so gentle with their lambs.

Fiver managed to feed all three of hers, without any need of a bottle to 'top up' the third lamb, which I had heard farmers would often suggest was necessary, if indeed they allowed the third lamb to stay with its mother at all. Mind you, considering the amount Fiver ate, this should not have come as a surprise. She was without doubt the greediest sheep I have ever encountered and was seemingly insatiable.

With the arrival of spring, the ewes and lambs went out onto grass together for the first time and the lambs were soon skipping about and generally carrying on with each other. But if they wandered too far away, the mothers would call them back to safety and the lambs would obediently return. It always made me smile at feed time, when the ewes were busy being fed, how the lambs would get mixed up and separated from their mother and run around in panic until they were reunited again.

In no time it was summer and I decided to have a go at showing my sheep at some of the shows. I had acquired a further Ryeland ram, called Titan. He was another big softie and I was delighted that Mr Universe and he got on so well together. Where one was, the other was never far away - they even slept together. I bought halters and began walking with them in the paddocks.

Both Mr Universe and Titan were used to a halter, as both had attended shows, but I wanted also to show a ewe and lambs in one of the classes which meant training a lamb with a halter. Anyone who has tried to train a puppy to walk on a lead will know how difficult this can be in the early stages.

I had no idea just how high a lamb could jump into the air. Nor had I bargained for the lying down, the flat refusal to stand up and, most worryingly, the frothing at the mouth, at the first sign of which one had to stop and abandon any further training for the day. But I persevered and practised each day until I had all four Ryeland ewes and their lambs halter trained just two weeks before the Cumberland Show.

The next task was to bathe them and, as I did not have a sheep bath, the only way to approach this was to tie up the sheep and use a sponge and bucket. And so, with the help of two neighbours, Pat and her daughter, half a dozen boxes of Lux flakes and gallons of warm water, Mr Universe, Titan and the Ryeland ewes (but not their lambs) were sponged and scrubbed to look like new.

The only trouble was that each time we had got one of them nice and clean, you could guarantee that the wretched animal would go and find the most dirty bit of land to lie on and, within minutes, we would have to begin all over again. By the end, it would have been fair to say that the three of us were wetter than the sheep and the whole scene was reminiscent of one of those rounds from *It's a Knockout*, only without Stuart Hall laughing down the microphone at the hapless contestants.

The day of my first show arrived and a kind friend transported all of the Ryelands to Carlisle where they were put in four pens: Mr Universe in one, Titan in another, two ewes and lambs in each of the other two. The adult ram class came first and I led Mr Universe into the ring, while my friend followed with Titan.

Handlers and rams all stood in line and took turns to respond to the judge's individual commands. First, one handler and ram would be asked to parade up and down and then another, while the rest of us, handlers and rams, waited expectantly - all of us that is except for Mr Universe.

Before going into the ring, I had taken the precaution of filling both pockets of my white coat with his favourite digestive biscuits, knowing that so long as a biscuit was in the offing I could usually persuade Mr Universe to do what I wanted. He was quite happy standing in line, while I surreptitiously slipped him a biscuit, and quite happy to take his turn to walk up and down for the judge's inspection with the inducement of a further biscuit.

But the judging was taking so long that, after another walk up and down, Mr Universe was starting to lose interest in the proceedings and, finding himself required to stand in line yet again, very sensibly thought he would be far more comfortable sitting down instead.

'Get up!' I hissed, as I felt his bulk descending towards the ground, and managed to hold him up with the aid of another dangled biscuit, 'You're not showing me up in front of all these people.'

The biscuit earned me a brief respite but he was soon shuffling about again and trying to sit. I was down to my last biscuit and, after that had gone, it was a trial of strength between him and me or, to be more precise, strength on his part and will power on mine.

Fortunately, just at the point where it seemed that strength was going to have the edge over will power, the judge walked over to Mr Universe and placed a hand on his head. Having realised that this particular hand was a biscuit free zone, Mr Universe looked at the judge with complete disdain, but at least the action was enough to keep him still while the judge handed me a blue rosette. Mr Universe had won second prize in my first appearance at a show.

We withdrew from the ring and Mr Universe retired to his pen, where he spent the rest of the afternoon tucking into a bale of hay, which we had brought with us, and which he ate lying down.

That was not the only success of the day because Titan had been

awarded third prize in the ram class and later one of the ewes was awarded second prize in the class for ewes with lamb at foot.

It was in this latter category that my lack of experience told again
because it had not occurred to me in advance of the show that all four
ewes and their lambs would have to enter the ring at the same time. My
friend and I could only manage one pair each and I had to resort to asking two spectators if they would mind bringing in the other pairs.

However, that was as nothing compared to my mistake over the 'Prime
Lamb' class in which I had entered two of my earliest and biggest lambs.
While all the sheep were in their pens, one of the other Ryeland owners
said that she had noticed I had a couple of entries in this class.

'Which ones are the prime lambs?' she asked.

'Those two,' I replied pointing towards one of the pens.

She started to laugh. 'Do you know what happens to the prime lambs?'

'No.'

'Well, you see those men with scales over there? They come and
weigh the lambs and then the butchers take them away at the end of the
show to the abattoir and they get sold as best butchers' lamb.'

'What!' I shouted, 'Keep an eye on these for me will you please, while
I find the steward.'

I am not sure how, but I found the steward almost immediately.

'I am sorry,' I said, 'but there has been a mistake. I wish to withdraw
my two entries in the prime lamb class.'

The steward looked slightly taken aback but, after a pause, said simply, 'Okay,' checked their numbers on his list and drew a line through
them.

I had thought naively that the 'prime lamb' category was simply for
good-looking lambs. It had never occurred to me that this might mean
lambs that would look good in gravy with mint sauce.

On the subject of good looks, I realised from watching the other sheep
at the show and from talking to their handlers that I had overdone it on
the washing and grooming. I had my sheep dressed and brushed like
poodles and, believe it or not, some of them were actually too white. Still,
I had not done badly for a beginner and my confidence was boosted at
the Dumfries show where again I did quite well, managing to get a place

for each sheep entered. However, since that was the only other show within easy travelling distance, I did not bother with any more that year. Instead I set my sights on achieving great things in 2000.

4

STEPHEN

As the Millennium approached and my ewes were in lamb, I wondered how I could cut down on the nightly patrols to the shed and if there might be a better alternative to using the baby alarm. One night, lying awake in bed thinking about the sheep (no use counting them to help me go to sleep), it occurred to me that close circuit television might be the answer.

So, the following morning it was off to B&Q to look for something suitable. I came back with a close circuit television camera, which I rigged up in the shed and connected to an old black and white television set in my bedroom. The pictures were not too bad - well up to 1950s Outside Broadcast standard - and I had sound as well. But at least I could switch that off, so as to avoid setting off Chloe barking, and still look at the screen. It worked a treat, so long as the ewe I wanted to keep an eye on was in view of the camera, and I was able to cut down on the nightly trips.

I celebrated the arrival of 2000 quietly with my animals. In fact, with the noise of the fireworks all around and the reaction of the dogs, it was not that quiet but it was in the sense that I did not have any of the family with me. Instead my four boys, Stephen, Peter, Tim and Andrew had gathered together in Newcastle to see in the New Year and were down among the revellers on the Quayside. Only Stephen and Tim were still based in Newcastle. Peter was working in Oxford and Andrew in London. But I was pleased that they had all managed to get together to greet the Millennium and they telephoned in high spirits to wish me a Happy New Year.

Lambing that spring went quite smoothly and, judging from the size of the lambs, I felt confident that I would have some that I could enter in that year's shows alongside their mothers and my two stars, Mr Universe and Titan. Prospects for the year looked promising.

One morning Radio Cumbria telephoned me and said that they wanted to do a feature on a hobby farmer and would I be interested in taking part. The description of 'hobby farmer' is one I dislike intensely because it suggests an activity that you do in your spare time for enjoyment and relaxation. While it is certainly true that I enjoy looking after my animals and that I do not depend upon them for my livelihood in the way that a commercial farmer does, nevertheless looking after animals properly is a time consuming business and often far from relaxing. My idea of a hobby is something you can pick up or put down when you feel like it. You cannot behave like that with animals. They are a commitment day in and day out, whether you feel like it or not. However, the caller sounded nice and, as I am always happy to show off my sheep and talk about them, I overlooked the use of the word 'hobby' and said yes.

The contact from Radio Cumbria came about because I had done some occasional 'cat sitting' for a couple, Clare and Neil, who both worked for the station. Apparently there had been a meeting where the idea of doing an interview with a 'hobby farmer' or a smallholder, the latter being my preferred description, had been discussed and they had suggested my Ryeland sheep as a suitable subject.

It was more than twenty years since I had last done a radio broadcast and I had forgotten what a nerve racking business it can be to try and answer questions with a microphone stuck in front of your face. However, the sheep showed no sign of nerves and they bleated in all the right places into the reporter's microphone, so that she had plenty of appropriate sound effects. She was amused at the classical names that I had given some of the sheep and amazed that they actually answered to them when called. As always, Mr Universe made a big impression and the reporter finished by saying that he really did live up to his name. The programme was broadcast the following day and little did I realise then that this would be the first of many occasions when Mr Universe and my Ryelands would attract the attentions of the media.

I decided that I would book in for as many shows as possible because both my rams were in excellent condition and the lambs were little crackers. I began halter training the lambs and after many painstaking hours I was pleased with the results of my schooling. I felt confident that this year we were all going to do very well.

The first show on my schedule was the Royal Lancashire, which was held at Chorley. Since this was a good four hours drive, I had borrowed a large trailer, as I only had a small one. The night before I packed all that was needed: feeding dishes, sheep cake, digestive biscuits, a bale of hay, halters and brushes. There was only just enough room in the car for some sandwiches and flasks of tea. I had asked a friend, Norman, if he would come with me, since I had never before towed a large trailer and I knew I would need assistance on the journey there and back, quite apart from help at the show itself. We agreed that we would have to set off at the crack of sparrows, as the sheep had to be penned by nine o'clock. I went to bed early so as to be on top form for the following day.

I was awoken by the telephone ringing at about two o'clock in the morning. It was Jane, my eldest son Stephen's partner. At first I could not make out what she was trying to tell me and then it hit me.

Stephen was dead.

Out of my four sons Stephen was always the dare devil and he had a passion for speed, both fast cars and equally fast motor bikes. He was in a local motor bike racing club and had won several cups. But he had always wanted to go one stage further and his motor bike partner had persuaded him to ride sidecar at the Isle of Man TT Races. He and his friend had been on a last practice run the evening before the races started and the bike had skidded on a bend. Stephen was thrown from the sidecar, flung up into the air and landed on a signpost. He had died in the ambulance helicopter on the way to the hospital.

If tomorrow starts without me,
And I'm not there to see,
If the sun should rise and find your eyes
All filled with tears for me.

I wish so much you wouldn't cry
The way you did today,
While thinking of the many things
We didn't get to say.

I know how much you love me,
As much as I love you,
And each time that you think of me
I know you'll miss me too.

But when tomorrow starts without me,
Please try to understand
That an angel came and called my name
And took me by the hand

And said my place was ready
In heaven far above
And that I'd have to leave behind
All those I dearly love.

But as I turned to walk away
A tear fell from my eye
For all my life I'd always thought
I didn't want to die.

I had so much to live for,
So much left yet to do.
It seemed almost impossible
That I was leaving you.

I thought of all the yesterdays,
The good times and the bad,
The thought of all the love we shared
And all the fun we had.

If I could relive yesterday,
Just even for a while,
I'd say good-bye and kiss you
And maybe see you smile.

But then I fully realised
That this could never be
For emptiness and memories
Would take the place of me.

But when I walked through Heaven's gates
I felt so much at Home.
When God looked down and smiled at me
From His great golden throne

He said, 'This is eternity
And all I've promised you.
Today your life on earth is passed,
But here life starts anew.

'You have always been so faithful,
So trusting and so true,
Though there were times you did
Some things you shouldn't do.

'But you have been forgiven
And now at last you're free.
So won't you come and take my hand
And share your life with me?'

So when tomorrow starts without me
Don't think we're far apart
For every time you think of me
I'm right here in your heart.

The author of these verses is unknown but they have been a great comfort to me when thinking of Stephen.

It seemed impossible that someone so full of life and someone who really had lived his life to the full, if not indeed to overflow, could have been taken from us so suddenly. He was very much the practical joker in the family, to the extent that when he was carrying on you would have thought he was the youngest of the boys as opposed to being the eldest. But he was also deeply caring and would help anyone in trouble. We were very close, more like sister and brother than mother and son.

Jane asked me if I would contact my mother and father and break the news to them. As they live about eighty miles away from me, I had to do this by telephone. I then had to ring each of my sons in turn: first, Peter in Oxford, then Tim in Newcastle and finally Andrew in London.

I was numb with shock and disbelief. My friend, Norman, arrived to drive with me to the show and I remember thinking that, yes, I would go and that I would win for Stephen. Some years ago, when CB radio first became a craze in the UK, Stephen, Peter and I had all got heavily involved and the call sign that I had adopted (quite prophetically, as it turned out) was Little Bo Peep. Stephen had thought it a huge joke that now I really did have some sheep to look after, except that he thought it unlikely I would lose any. But now I had lost him.

I said nothing to my friend and we loaded the sheep on to the trailer and set off for Chorley. I cannot remember anything about that journey except that we arrived late and the other handlers were already wearing their white coats ready for the judging in the ram section. I put the halter onto Mr Universe and Norman put a halter onto Titan and we all went into the ring. As we did so, Norman, who had been looking at the rival rams, nodded towards Mr Universe and said to me under his breath, 'There isn't one here to touch him.'

The judge came over to me and asked me to walk Mr Universe to the other end of the ring. He kept going away and coming back to me, feeling Mr Universe's back and looking him up and down. Mr Universe, for his part, was behaving impeccably and looking very majestic. Eventually the steward went to the judge holding the rosettes and came back with a big red rosette, which he handed to me. Mr Universe had been placed first.

Norman turned to me and said, 'You have done well.'

'You mean, Mr Universe has done well,' I replied.

As it happened, Titan (and Norman) had also done well, because Titan was awarded second place in the competition. We left the ring and returned to the pens, where I burst into tears. I had managed to get not only the first but also the second prize for Stephen.

I did not take any of my other sheep out for the classes in which I had entered them. It was too emotional. I sat in the pen with my sheep. However, because Mr Universe had won his class, later on I had to come out again with him, so as to be judged against the other Ryeland class winners for the accolade of 'best of breed'.

Unfortunately, having got into the ring, Titan could be heard blaring loudly from his pen. Mr Universe's ears pricked up at the familiar sound of his friend and fellow ram. Whether it was a cry for help or just an interesting piece of sheep gossip I do not know, but Mr Universe decided that he had to see Titan immediately and that he did not have time to hang about waiting for another judge to wander up and down, particularly if all he stood to get was another of those useless rosette things instead of a tasty digestive biscuit. He turned to head back towards the pens dragging me behind. I struggled to pull him back towards the other sheep, who were now all lined up for inspection, but my efforts were in vain and in the end there was nothing for it but to try and withdraw from the ring as gracefully as possible. The judges had no option but to disqualify Mr Universe from the rankings for 'best of breed'. If I had let Norman go into the ring in my place, he would have been strong enough to master Mr Universe, who might then have won the prize for the best Ryeland. But I was satisfied with what we had achieved.

I had to arrange for someone to look after my sheep and the other animals so that I could travel across to Newcastle for Stephen's funeral. The service was held at St Mary's Church in Forest Hall, which in itself brought back memories because it was at this church that both Stephen and Peter had once been altar boys. To be truthful, it was actually Peter who was the altar boy but, on one occasion, Stephen donned a surplice as well so that I could take a photograph of both of them looking suitably angelic.

The church was packed and many of the congregation had to stand at the back. I learnt afterwards that Stephen's workplace had shut for the morning and that two coaches had been hired to bring his colleagues to the church. There were friends from the biking community, friends who had travelled up from Oxford and friends from his school days. I was touched that so many people had come.

I stood at the front with the rest of the family. Jane and Stephen had three children but it was decided that only Amy, who was nine, should attend the service. The two boys, Ben and Mikey, were only three and two years old respectively and were kept away. But the most poignant sight was that of Stephen's three brothers, acting as pallbearers to his coffin along with three of his closest friends, and Stephen's motor bike helmet resting on the lid.

After the service, we all drove to the crematorium with an escort of six outriders on motor bikes. Given the circumstances of his death, neither Jane nor I had been particularly happy about this idea but we accepted that it was meant as a heartfelt tribute by his biking friends and we understood that it was something which Stephen himself would have wanted. It certainly meant that his final journey was carried out in some style.

I remember nothing about the journey home to Warwick Bridge and little about the following days. Cards and letters of condolence kept arriving but I must have been in denial because I put each one in a drawer unopened and it was a long time before I could bring myself to look at them. I spent as much time as possible out of doors and it would sometimes be quite dark before I could bring myself to go inside. Often I broke down in tears, sitting beside my sheep. They seemed to understand that something was wrong and would come and nuzzle into me, while staring into my eyes. I found this very therapeutic and became more and more attached to my sheep, as they helped me over the worst hurdle in my life.

Because I had managed to rent a large field immediately behind the cottage, I was under no pressure of space for animals and I decided to keep all my lambs that year. Someone suggested that I should buy some Scotch Blacks, as they lambed on their own, were very good mothers and, I was told, no trouble whatsoever. So I bought some cheap. They were not the youngest of sheep. 'Broken mouthed' was the term used, which meant that they did not have many of their teeth left. The plan was to put them into lamb with one of my Ryeland Rams and then sell them on later as ewes with lambs at foot, using the proceeds to pay for the rental of the field.

The 'Blackies' arrived straight from the hills in Scotland and to say that they were wild would be an understatement. Not only were they quite unused to people, they were quite unused to other sheep and kept as far away as possible from the Ryelands. Any onlooker would have assumed that there must have been an electric fence separating the two flocks. Whenever I went into the field the separation became even more marked. While the Ryelands would come charging towards me like a herd of mini buffalo, admittedly outstripped by the two Leicesters, Topsy and Fiver, who had the advantage of longer legs, the Scotch Blacks would sprint off in the opposite direction and take refuge in the farthest corner of the field.

Now every so often sheep need worming and their feet need trimming (just like a cat needs to be wormed and have its claws clipped from time to time). With the Ryelands this was not a problem, but it was quite another story with the Blackies. In the end, I had to get Norman and his collie dog to assist me in rounding them up for treatment. Trying to do anything with them was a nightmare and, having got rid of my gander from hell, these sheep most definitely took his place as being the sheep from hell.

Nonetheless by late autumn that year, all of the Blackies were in lamb, so they must have stopped running and stood still long enough for one of the rams! As winter began and the grass had stopped growing, I thought that they would calm down a little and might be coaxed to come near me by the prospect of hay and sheep cake. Certainly they ran towards me once they realised that the Ryelands were eating something tasty, but they would stop at least ten foot short and, at the slightest sudden movement, they would turn and tear back to the other end of the field, where they would remain staring at me until I left the scene. Only after I had gone would the Blackies return and move tentatively towards the troughs containing the hay and sheep cake. Even then, I noticed that there was always one of them who seemed to have been posted on look out duty, just in case I was spotted coming back.

It was clear that my Ryelands were completely bemused by the behaviour of their immigrant neighbours and, in time, the wariness with which the Blackies had always treated them was reciprocated. It was rather as if they were two peoples forced into a state of uneasy co-existence, because each recognised that neither side outnumbered the other. That winter I had what could be described as a state of 'cold war' between sheep in my own backyard. But it was a state which I could tolerate and which did not threaten any harm.

As I came to the end of what had been a year of personal tragedy for my family and me, I could not have imagined that the following year was to bring tragedy on a far wider and unprecedented scale for so many more families - and their animals.

5

FOOT AND MOUTH

The year 2001 started sadly. At New Years Eve my thoughts turned inevitably to Stephen and the year that was passing. It was hard to believe that he would not be telephoning to wish me a Happy New Year and it did not help that his birthday was only four days later.

I was relieved to have got through the beginning of January and yet again found that having the sheep and the rest of my animal family to care for was a great comfort. After the experience of previous years, I was more organised on the lambing front and I knew that my Ryelands were unlikely to start lambing before March and that the Blackies were not due until April.

February arrived and I was all prepared for lambing, having ticked off my checklist of antibiotics, lamb milk and other accessories. The latter included a pair of powerful binoculars so that from the window on the landing I could survey the field behind and keep an eye on the Blackies, as they roamed from one end to the other.

I also needed to keep an eye on the Ryelands, not because of their wandering off like the Blackies but in case any of them ended up on their backs and could not get up again.

Ryelands are heavily built at the best of times and a pregnant Ryeland with the extra weight of carrying one or more lambs is definitely at the worst of times. If a pregnant ewe lies down on uneven ground and goes into a deep sleep (and, believe you me, Ryelands snore), the risk is that she will then roll onto her side. On awaking she will then scrape at the ground to try and stand up, but with her short, stumpy legs she can easily roll over on to her back and become completely helpless - what I learnt is known in Cumbria as 'kessing'.

One day, late in February, I came indoors to make a cup of tea and heard on the radio that foot and mouth disease had been confirmed among some pigs at an abattoir in Essex. Geography is not my strong point but even I knew that Essex was very near London and that London was a very long way from Cumbria, so I did not give this news a great deal of thought. I had vague memories of the foot and mouth outbreak in the late 1960s but, living in a city at the time and far from the scene, I had paid little attention to this and knew nothing about the disease and its impact on farms and the countryside. I was a typical townie.

Three days later came news from somewhere altogether closer to home. Foot and mouth had been confirmed on a pig farm at Heddon-on-the-Wall in Northumberland. I did not need a map to know where Heddon was - only 30 miles from the Cumbrian border and less than 50 miles from me.

Furthermore it was being suggested that this pig farm might be the source of the earlier outbreak, because the farm was apparently a meat supplier to the abattoir in Essex. A five-mile exclusion zone had been imposed around the farm by MAFF (the Ministry of Agriculture, Fisheries and Food) and all the animals had been slaughtered.

The Minister for Agriculture, Nick Brown, announced a seven day ban on livestock movements and the closure of all auction marts. Countryside events were being cancelled and walkers urged to stay away from the Lake District.

I decided that I ought to read up about foot and mouth. I had acquired several books about keeping and looking after sheep but I noticed that those that had been published recently had little or nothing to say about the disease. By contrast, an old book on the recognition and treatment of common sheep ailments (note the adjective 'common'), which my mother had found in a charity shop and given me, not only contained detailed information but also some helpful pictures. It was called the *TV Vet Sheep Book*.

Foot and mouth, I discovered from the TV Vet, is caused by 'a filtrable virus which multiplies and spreads rapidly. During an outbreak the sheep eat the virus. It gets into the bloodstream and travels to the mouth, nostrils, feet and occasionally the udder. On these sites the virus multiplies underneath the skin to produce blisters which burst and discharge millions of the viruses on to the pasture.

'The blisters on the udder, nostrils and mouth are usually small and difficult to see', continued the TV Vet, 'In the mouth they form on the dental pad, inside the lips or on the tongue.'

The TV Vet moved on to describe the symptoms, 'The flock becomes generally dull and many of them stop grazing,' he said, as if he were a schoolmaster describing what might happen to a class of dim schoolboys who had given up trying, 'Shortly afterwards widespread lameness develops.'

Then, in a more technical tone of voice, 'The lameness is due to the tenderness of the ruptured blisters and to secondary ulceration and infection. Close examination will reveal the blisters or ulcers around the top of and between the claws or at the base of the supernumerary digits.'

I was not immediately sure what the TV Vet meant by 'supernumerary digits'. My dictionary (*Collins Gem*) defined 'supernumerary' as 'exceeding the required or regular number' and a 'digit' as a 'finger or toe'. Surely the TV Vet was not suggesting that a sheep developed extra toes as a result of foot and mouth? I realised that he must be talking about the soft pads behind the claws that sheep have in place of toes.

'There may be similar lesions on the dental pad, inside the lips or on the tongue; with a very occasional blister on the udder,' were the TV Vet's final comments on the symptoms.

'Any suspect case must be reported to the police or to your veterinary surgeon immediately,' advised the TV Vet, 'Having done so, you must on no account leave your farm until the authorities allow you to do so.'

And then the chilling conclusion about treatment, 'If a case is confirmed, the entire flock and all contact cloven hoofed animals will be slaughtered.'

I was scared. The *TV Vet Sheep Book* might have been published many years ago but it was already clear from the news that the recommended approach to combating foot and mouth had not changed during the intervening years. There was no cure. Slaughter was still considered to be the only answer.

I gazed out at the field and at the sheep grazing peacefully. None of them looked listless - quite the reverse in fact. None of them appeared to be limping. Surely they were going to be all right? But I had better go out and check.

And so my existing twice daily routine, of going out into the field to check on the sheep, was extended to include the regular inspection of feet and mouths for blisters, while the binocular surveys for 'kessing' Ryelands and roaming Blackies now focussed first and foremost on any sign of lameness, no matter what the breed of sheep.

I did not know any farmers to whom I could talk apart from my friends Pam and Keith, who had taken some of my lambs in the past. I knew that Keith would be in regular contact with local farmers and would be able to pass on any news and so I telephoned him. Keith was very concerned about the situation and advised me to keep any visitors well away. This was not too much of a problem for me, as I had relatively few visitors and those that came had no association with farms and farming. However, I did go out and get a stock of disinfectant and some buckets, so as to comply with the bio security measures insisted on by MAFF.

I placed one bucket of disinfectant and a mat soaked in disinfectant by the small gate at the start of the path leading up to my front door and another bucket of disinfectant by the side of my main gate leading on to my drive. That, I thought to myself, should take care of any human visitors. But I needed also to do something for any visiting vehicles. Fortunately I still had some old carpet left over from doing up the cottage and so I dragged some of this to the entrance in front of my main gate. I soaked the carpet in disinfectant and continued to do so twice daily.

My Ryelands were getting near to lambing and I decided to bring them all indoors and keep them inside my shed. I did not have enough space to house the Blackies and anyway, since they are hill sheep, I knew that they would not relish being kept in a confined space. So they were left out in the field and from then onwards the two flocks were kept entirely separate from each other.

I read in a newspaper a letter from a farmer of how during the previous outbreak in the sixties he had fed Borax to his sheep via their drinking water. I tried all over Cumbria to find some of this but to no avail. Eventually I tracked down a supplier in London called Ainsworths and telephoned to order a large bottle. It arrived by special delivery the following day.

Inside the box was a leaflet proclaiming that Ainsworths were 'The First Name in Homeopathy, Chemists by Appointment to Her Majesty the Queen and the Queen Mother and Suppliers of Homeopathic Medicines to His Royal Highness the Prince of Wales.' Nothing but the best for my sheep, I thought to myself.

Attached to the invoice was a note on 'directions for use of borax 30c' as follows, 'Borax has been used in previous Foot and Mouth episodes (in 1939 and 1967). We cannot make claims as to how successful the use of Borax is. However, the following regime has been based on experience with other forms of homeopathic prevention: Two capfuls (about 10ml) should be added to a trough of drinking water or a spray bottle or fogging machine filled with water and agitated. The dose to be given daily for three days initially, then twice weekly for the duration of the epidemic.'

I did not have a fogging clue what a fogging machine was, if you will pardon my French, but I began straightaway to add Borax to the drinking water for all my sheep and continued on a daily basis rather than the twice weekly set down in the directions. In the case of the Blackies out in the field, the Borax went into a drinking trough but the Ryelands in the shed had individual buckets of water in each pen. I was not taking any chances.

March came and with it confirmation of the first cases of foot and mouth in Cumbria. They were centred on Longtown, whose auction mart had been linked previously with the movement of animals to other parts of the country where foot and mouth had already broken out. By that first weekend, the local *News & Star* was reporting that Cumbria was the worst hit county in the United Kingdom, with eleven confirmed cases and more suspected outbreaks emerging daily.

There was particular concern about the latter because the practice of MAFF was to wait until a case had been confirmed before naming the farm in question. Since this could be several days after infection had been suspected, it was feared that in the meantime people could have visited mistakenly and unnecessarily infected land and so helped unwittingly with the spread of the disease.

However, it soon became clear that this was not the only concern about the way in which MAFF was approaching the crisis. There was a very real problem with handling the cases that had been identified. By the second weekend of March, the *Cumberland News* was reporting that the number of animals infected by foot and mouth in Cumbria was rising faster than MAFF could cope with and the Ministry had suspended the slaughter of infected animals because it lacked the manpower to dispose of the carcasses.

There was a heartbreaking report that a Longtown farmer had had his 800 animals left lying dead on his land for five days after they had been shot and that trenches, where they were to be placed for incineration, were still being dug. Another report was of a farm at Tirril where a pyre of carcasses had burned for three days and the smoke could be seen clearly from Beacon Edge near Penrith and for many miles around.

David Maclean, the Conservative MP for Penrith and the Borders, whose constituency was very much (and literally) in the firing line, was reported as telling the Agriculture Minister, Nick Brown, in the House of Commons that the situation in Cumbria was 'verging on out of control' and pleaded for extra help to speed up the testing and burning of animals, including the use of troops. Mr Brown's reported response was that the outbreak was under control but that more cash would be made available if MAFF's chief veterinary officer said it was needed.

The local BBC station, Radio Cumbria, had started to provide a continuous information service on the development of foot and mouth, presented by Anne Hopper, who came out of retirement to do this. Every morning, I would listen to Anne read out the list of the latest farms where foot and mouth had been confirmed and the list got longer and longer. If I had missed any, I would turn to Ceefax on the television, where the pages showing dates and farms seemed to go on and on.

As a newcomer to the county, I did not know Cumbria that well and I had never heard of some of the places mentioned on the radio by Anne or listed on Ceefax. I was forever telephoning Keith or other friends to ask where exactly was such and such a farm. How far was it from Carlisle? How far from Warwick Bridge? How far from my sheep?

Foot and mouth seemed to be spreading at an alarming rate. By the middle of March Cumbria was well on the way to having a hundred cases confirmed. The livestock industry was in complete crisis, auction marts were laying off staff and tourism was paralysed. David Maclean continued with his calls for troops to be brought in to help with the slaughter and disposal of diseased animals and said that a state of emergency should be declared. Nick Brown, the Agriculture Minister, continued to insist that the disease was under control.

I have never been a political person but I did wonder if Nick Brown would have reacted in quite the same way had David Maclean been a Labour MP or indeed if there had not been a widespread expectation that Tony Blair was going to call a general election for the beginning of May. Perhaps he was being misled by his officials at MAFF and genuinely thought that the situation was under control. Perhaps the officials at

MAFF genuinely thought that the situation was under control.

Whatever the reason, in a matter of days the cat was well and truly out of the bag - or one could say, quite appropriately in view of what happened, the cattle were out of the bag.

On the afternoon of what became known locally as Black Thursday, Nick Brown announced in the House of Commons that all animals residing within three kilometres of foot and mouth infected farms were to be culled in a final bid to halt the spread of the disease.

In Cumbria there was an immediate reaction of fury and despair. It was pointed out that such a policy would lay waste to a massive area between Longtown and Penrith. Thousands of apparently healthy animals would be condemned to death. Prize pedigree herds with irreplaceable bloodlines would be wiped out. Farmers were telephoning the NFU (National Farmers' Union) to say that their cattle would only be taken out over their dead bodies - and they meant their bodies, not those of their cattle.

Within hours of that announcement, the hapless Nick Brown had performed an apparent U-turn on the local Border TV news programme in the face of persistent questioning from its interviewer, Fiona Armstrong. Pressed over the plan to kill cattle, Brown told her 'not to shout' at him before disclosing that the three kilometre cull in fact applied only to sheep and pigs - not to cattle.

The following day Nick Brown apologised to farmers for ambiguities in his statement to the Commons that had led hundreds of them to believe that their cattle would face mass slaughter. He said he would travel to Cumbria as soon as possible to meet farmers and clear up any misunderstanding about the government's policy. Speaking from MAFF headquarters in London he was reported as saying, 'I want to apologise on my own behalf and behalf of the Ministry for any hurt this has caused farmers. We didn't explain ourselves very well yesterday. Having re-read my statement it is accurate but I can see that it is ambiguous.'

Whether or not Nick Brown's statement had been ambiguous about cattle did not concern me personally. What was absolutely clear was that sheep, whether healthy or not, were to be culled if they were unfortunate enough to be in an area within three kilometres of an infected farm. There was no ambiguity about that whatsoever.

I was distraught. At a stroke the risk of my sheep being caught up in this evolving holocaust had been multiplied.

The thought of my sheep being infected by foot and mouth was bad enough. Since the outbreak, I had just about come to reconcile myself to the fact that if, despite all my stringent precautions, they did go down with the disease, then I would have no choice but to have them slaughtered and taken away to burn on a funeral pyre. At least I would know that they had been infected and had been put out of their misery, even though the method of doing so was like something out of the Dark Ages.

But to think that my sheep might have to be culled, while not showing signs of being anything other than well, simply because of being inside an arbitrarily chosen area of three kilometres, this was too much. Why three kilometres, as opposed to three and a half or two and a half? What was so scientific about the distance chosen? If the far end of my field was caught within three kilometres of an infected farm could I let the Blackies go, but keep the Ryelands on the grounds that they were outside the zone because of being safely in the shed? Could I appeal against any decision to cull my sheep? Could I stop MAFF officials coming on to my land? These and many other questions raced through my mind.

The prospect of losing Mr Universe and Titan, Topsy and Fiver, the Ryeland ewes and even the Blackies was just too dreadful to contemplate. But even more distressing was the fact that my Ryelands had started to lamb and the realisation that I might lose newly born lambs, as well as unborn lambs still inside their mothers.

Since mathematics is no more of a strong point with me than geography, I had first to ask someone to work out for me the area over which I was potentially at risk from neighbouring farms. I was mildly reassured to discover that one did not have to go too far before being out of range. Even so, there were still too many other farms nearby for comfort.

What should I do? I was sick and tired of being a virtual prisoner in my own home, sick and tired of waiting for what might or might not happen, sick and tired of not knowing whether I was going to come through or end up with nothing.

I decided that I had to do something positive if only to keep my sanity. My sheep had helped me get through the worst experience of my life in losing my eldest son the year before. It was my turn to help them.

I resolved to fight back.

6

FIGHTING BACK

Resolving to fight back was one thing. Deciding on how to go about this was quite another. Many years ago, I had been involved in founding and working for the Tyneside branch of the Cyrenians, a national organisation that tried to help men who had fallen on hard times and who were 'down and out'. We had started with a nightly soup run on the Newcastle Quayside, graduated to a night shelter within shouting distance of Newcastle United's football ground and then acquired houses in Walker and Gateshead, where some men could stay on a short term basis and learn to live again as members of the community before finding their own accommodation and rejoining society.

At various times, I had made use of the local press to help promote the work of the Cyrenians and I had always found them helpful, despite the fact that it would be fair to say that stories about down and outs were not calculated to arouse much sympathy among the general public. I wondered whether the press and the general public would show any more sympathy for an isolated smallholder and her threatened sheep.

As it happened I was not the only one. My friend Keith had been given a card by someone at the Press Association, who was looking for 'human interest' stories connected with foot and mouth, and Keith passed on the card to me. I telephoned the Press Association in Newcastle upon Tyne and told them of my plight. They asked if they could come out to do an interview that very afternoon. This was only the Saturday immediately after Nick Brown's Black Thursday.

The man from the Press Association arrived with his camera. He was called Owen. He assured me that he had not been on any farms infected by foot and mouth, but nevertheless I made sure that he stepped in the disinfectant bucket before coming on to my land. It was quite a cold afternoon and I was wearing an old woolly hat, which covered my ears.

I let out my two Ryeland rams, Mr Universe and Titan, into a small paddock for a photo call. Owen showed great patience with them before taking a few photographs. It was quite a job to usher the rams back indoors again. They seemed to enjoy the attention, not to mention the rare opportunity to be outside.

Owen followed me to the door of the shed and asked if I would pick up one of the lambs and bring it to the entrance, so that he could photograph me holding it, without him coming inside and disturbing the Ryelands. As I did so, I could not help thinking of what might happen to my sheep and had difficulty in holding back the tears. Owen calmly snapped away. He made some notes about the Ryelands, in particular the fact that they were a rare breed, wished me good luck and went on his way. Subsequently, his boss at the PA, Paul, telephoned to check various details. Paul turned out to come from Sunderland, so there was some good-natured argument about him being a Mackem reporting on the troubles of a Geordie.

The result of this approach to the Press Association exceeded my wildest expectations. I had thought that my story would be picked up by the local press and so it proved when I saw Monday morning's *Journal* which, although Newcastle based, has a daily readership extending across the North of England. However, as they say, a picture can be worth a thousand words and one of Owen's photographs of me holding the new lamb had clearly struck a chord with more than one newspaper editor. There I was or, I should say, there we were, reproduced in black and white in Monday's issues of the *Daily Mail*, the *Daily Express* and Scotland's the *Herald*, to name only three.

But the *piece de resistance* was in none other than the *Times*. Not only did they publish my or, I should say, our photograph in colour on page 8 - although there was precious little colour in my face apart from redness around the eyes - but on the front page was another of Owen's photographs, this time a close up of Mr Universe and Titan, with the strapline 'Rare Ryeland sheep from Cumbria could be spared.'

It turned out that my story and photographs had coincided with a move on the part of MAFF to further limit the extent of the three kilometre culling policy announced the week before. 'Owners of specialist pedigree and rare breed flocks in Cumbria', reported the *Times*, next to the photograph of Mr Universe and Titan, 'are to be allowed a right of appeal against a cull. The lifeline, announced by Jim Scudamore, the Government Chief Veterinary Officer, is designed to quell the threat of revolt from communities angry at last week's orders to slaughter healthy animals. He will disclose this limited concession to farmers and vets in meetings in the county today.'

The meeting to which the *Times* referred was held at the Shepherds Inn, Rosehill, which is on the edge of Carlisle. Since this was barely three miles away, I thought I would go along. There was only a small group of protesters gathered and when Jim Scudamore arrived they greeted him with a slow hand clap. As a result of my coverage in the morning's newspapers, I was recognised by some of the reporters present and collected a handful of business cards. But I managed to keep out of range of the photographers and did not stay for long. I never liked to spend more than an hour away from the cottage and my sheep, if I could possibly avoid it.

When I got back the telephone was soon ringing and I spoke in turn to the Carlisle *News & Star*, the *Cumberland News*, BBC *Look North* and Border TV.

That evening's *News & Star* reported how farmers had told chief vet Scudamore that he should, 'sort out the sick before culling our healthy sheep.' But it also reported that government policy had not changed, that the slaughter was expected to start later in the week and, furthermore, that the process had started already across the border in Scotland, 'where around 1,800 apparently healthy sheep were killed yesterday.'

I thought of Susan Bryden in Lockerbie and her Ryeland flock, including of course Mr Universe's father, and I wondered if they would survive. For some reason, opposition in Dumfries and Galloway to the three kilometre culling policy seemed far less vocal than in Cumbria and I feared for their safety.

Events of the following day were to heighten dramatically fears for the safety of my own sheep. As normal, I tuned into Radio Cumbria to hear the list of latest confirmed outbreaks and to my horror one of those mentioned was Warwick Holme Farm.

I did not know anyone at Warwick Holme Farm. I had never been to Warwick Holme Farm. But I did know that Warwick Holme Farm was less than three kilometres from where I was at Warwick Bridge. Not much less admittedly - I worked out that the distance was actually about two and a half kilometres - but enough for there not to be any doubt on the matter.

I was inside a three kilometre culling zone.

I walked out of the cottage in a complete daze and across to the shed. By now all the Ryelands had lambed successfully and the shed was full to bursting point. Normally at this time all of the sheep would have been out on the grass and not locked inside a shed. Instead I had given the lambs some bales of straw to play on, as they loved jumping on and off things. I felt the tears trickle down my face as I looked on at the scene of gambolling lambs and thought about what might happen to them.

I wandered out of the shed and looked across to the field where the Blackies, all of them still to lamb, were grazing without an apparent care in the world. I tried to steel myself to the thought that, if it came to the crunch, I would let the Blackies go to be culled if it meant that I could keep the Ryelands. But then I thought of Topsy and Fiver. They were as dear to me as Mr Universe and Titan. If I made a point of distinguishing between the Ryelands, on the grounds that they were a rare breed, and the rest of my sheep, on the grounds that they were not, then that would mean Topsy and Fiver, and their lambs, having to go along with the Blackies. No, I said to myself, all of my sheep are healthy. None of them are going without a fight. It was going to be a case of 'one for all and all for one'.

My resolve was stiffened by the amazing response that I was receiving to all of the press publicity. Quite apart from the newspaper coverage, I learnt that the BBC News website had posted a long article with the head-line, 'Rare breeds could be lost' under which had been reproduced Owen's colour photograph of me in my woolly hat clutching the lamb. The article quoted me at length and linked my situation with comments from the chief executive of the Rare Breeds Survival Trust.

Cards and letters began arriving on a daily basis, despite the fact that many of the correspondents did not know my address. The Royal Mail did a wonderful job in coping with mail addressed to 'The Lady with Rare Breed Sheep' or, in one case, a photograph of me and my lamb with the simple plea 'Please Postman Find this Lady in Cumbria'.

Most were messages of support and encouragement but occasionally there was practical advice too. In particular, two days after I had been in the papers, I received a card from Christina, a nutritional practitioner in Newcastle, who had formerly farmed in Sweden. She recommended a cheap, biodegradable and safe anti-biotic which, she said, would totally inhibit the foot and mouth virus and which was called GSE Citricidal. This comprised grapefruit pip extract and small bottles could be obtained at many health shops. There was a telephone number on the card and I spoke to Christina. She offered to buy some bottles for me, as she could get them at trade price and drove across from Newcastle to deliver them in person.

I was still putting Borax in the sheep's water on a daily basis and now they were getting grapefruit pip extract in their sheep cake as well. I was prepared to try anything.

Another welcome and unusual card came from an artist in London, called Shireen Faircloth. She had seen the photograph of the lamb and me in the *Daily Mail* and wanted my permission to do a painting of us, which she could enter for the Royal Academy of Art summer school exhibition. There was apparently only a one in twelve chance of an entry being accepted. I telephoned her number and said I would be happy for her to do this. I prayed that it would not turn out to be a commemorative painting.

In the midst of all this, I was contacted by the production team of ITV's weekly current affairs programme, *Tonight with Trevor McDonald*. They were trying to line up a series of interviews with people who were directly affected by foot and mouth to feature in a special report by Michael Nicholson on the crisis in Cumbria. They already had a number of farmers and were looking for one or two smallholders. The fact that I had rare breed sheep was an additional attraction.

Well, I thought to myself, why not? I was sure Mr Universe would give a good account of himself on television and moreover we were talking national prime time television on a programme fronted by Britain's favourite newscaster. If I helped a TV camera crew now with a programme that they wanted to make, perhaps I would be able to get a TV camera crew to help me later when the men from MAFF arrived to cull my sheep.

Michael Nicholson and two members of the production team from Granada TV duly arrived in the road outside my cottage. I thought how appropriate it was that a journalist, who had reported on the Falklands War and just about every other conflict around the world since, was now reporting on what I had come to regard as our war zone in Cumbria. He was a very sympathetic interviewer and seemed to take to Mr Universe, who in turn certainly enjoyed being filmed, having realised that this meant receiving extra biscuits.

Michael Nicholson's sympathy for the plight of Cumbria generally came through strongly in the report that was broadcast that same week on *Tonight with Trevor McDonald*. The programme had hardly started before there was a brief close-up of me saying that the situation was, 'like living on a time bomb.' However, I found much of the subsequent report difficult to watch. There was harrowing film footage of cattle being shot and burnt and then of dead, diseased sheep left lying in a field, just before the programme cut to scenes of my live and healthy Ryelands enjoying a brief run in the paddock.

Then it was the turn of Mr Universe to accompany me down the path to be interviewed, although he was clearly more interested in the contents of the bright yellow bowl, which I was carrying, than he was in the camera. I talked of how my sheep all had names and individual personalities and how losing them would be as traumatic as losing a pet dog or cat, only more so because there were so many of them. I spoke of the lambs born in the last few days and my anxiety about how little time they might be allowed to live. All this time Mr Universe munched away at my side.

Michael Nicholson ended his report with a passionate condemnation of the inadequacy of the operation attempting to combat foot and mouth. He said that, before he had left London, he had been told that adequate safeguards and quarantine measures were in place. Well, he added, standing on a carpet of straw that should have been squelching with disinfectant but which was actually bone dry, he would earnestly suggest to the government that they send someone up to take a look at what was really going on.

As it happened, the government did send someone up. The Prime Minister himself made a surprise visit to Cumbria, en route to a conference in Stockholm, to meet farmers' leaders. A handful of soldiers had already been drafted in to help but now Tony Blair promised that MAFF and the Army could have whatever resources they felt necessary. It was announced that the culling of healthy animals inside a three kilometre radius of infected farms would start within days and that slaughter and disposal sites would be set up on disused airfields. Brigadier Alex Birtwistle was to take charge of the operation and over that weekend the Army dug a huge trench at Great Orton, an old military airfield, which was designed to be a mass grave for hundreds of thousands of sheep.

The Army had first to deal with a backlog of sheep carcasses that had been lying around for weeks but I realised that it would not be long before attention would turn to the removal and transportation of live sheep. I wondered how long it would take before I received a letter or a telephone call or even a visit about mine - and what I should do when I did. My mood ranged from anger to despair and back again.

On the one hand, I felt that at last with the Army now involved everything would be more under control than it had been and that there might be an end in sight. On the other hand, I could not believe that the policy of culling healthy animals could be right. It seemed such a costly, draconian and antiquated approach. Surely there had to be a better way.

I hardly dared leave the cottage for fear of something happening in my absence and, with time on my hands, I had started to read more and more about the issues surrounding foot and mouth. Vaccination was being proposed in many quarters as an alternative policy to culling but apparently such a step would play havoc with the export trade. I read an interview in the *Cumberland News* with a MAFF official in which he explained that the policy of slaughter granted a country 'disease free' status under the World Organisation for Animal Health rules. Without this status, farmers could not export and the export market last year had been worth an estimated £400 million.

'If the government introduced emergency vaccination,' said the MAFF official, 'export to Europe would be banned until we could claim to be disease-free, without vaccination, for 12 months. The vaccine is also not 100 per cent effective.'

I scratched my head at this. With foot and mouth having come so soon after the BSE crisis, I could not imagine anyone in Europe being very keen to take British exports, so would it not be better to vaccinate and get the disease under control? But quite apart from this, I was struck by the *Alice in Wonderland* argument of the Animal Health rules themselves, which seemed to be that an animal, which had not been vaccinated against foot and mouth, was automatically deemed to be healthier and safer than an animal that had been vaccinated.

As for the comment about the vaccine not being 100 per cent effective, I was fairly sure that this could be said about any vaccine for animals - or indeed humans.

From what I read, plenty of other countries around the world seemed to vaccinate their livestock as a matter of course against foot and mouth and, so far as I could judge, MAFF had done nothing since the previous outbreak in 1967 to look at alternative approaches to tackling the disease. I became more and more angry at what seemed to me inertia and incompetence on the part of a government department and I soon had an opportunity to give vent to my feelings.

I learnt that MAFF minister Nick Brown was at last paying his promised visit to Cumbria and that again the venue was the Shepherds Inn at Carlisle, just down the road. Susan Bull telephoned to say that she was going and I decided to join her. We stood with other protesters against the cull and I have to admit that I got rather carried away when Mr Brown emerged from his car and shouted out that he was a 'Murdering Bastard!' I do not have satellite TV but I was told that my outburst was recorded and shown on *Sky News*.

I dared not stay long and came away before Brown re-emerged to receive more jeers from the demonstrators outside. That evening's *News & Star* published a photograph of Susan and another friend, Amanda-Jane, shouting at Nick Brown, and I was quite relieved not to have been caught by the camera. Just at the moment I was not sure that I wanted to draw attention to myself. Brown was quoted as saying that he was actively considering vaccination in the battle against foot and mouth but that this was 'a matter of veterinary judgement, not political.' Perhaps there was some hope after all.

The following day I was back at the Shepherds Inn, this time to attend a meeting organised by a group called Farmers for Action, who had been calling for a policy of vaccination as an alternative to culling healthy livestock. David Hanley, a farmer from Devon, was to chair the meeting and the guest speaker was to be Dr Richard North, who was based in Brussels and acted as agricultural adviser to the UK Independence Party. More than two hundred people had turned up and the mood was a mixture of anger and fear. When I arrived there were still some seats free at the front row so I went and sat there.

David Hanley opened the meeting with a long speech. But his main point was to emphasise that, unless it could be shown that one's animals were infected with foot and mouth, culling of livestock was voluntary and therefore, if one's animals were indeed healthy, a farmer was quite entitled to resist any pressure to have his animals culled and could even refuse to allow MAFF officials on to his property.

Richard North then spoke in great detail about the nature of foot and mouth and how it should be tackled. He explained that, for sheep, foot and mouth was not actually a serious disease. It was like a flu virus and if sheep did go down with it they would be feverish and off colour, just as humans are with an attack of flu. But, with care and attention they could be expected to make a full recovery after no more than a week or so.

With both cattle and pigs the disease was much more serious and consequently infection from sheep was a risk that could not be taken lightly. Nevertheless he commented that, in many other parts of the world, farm animals were vaccinated as a matter of routine policy and he argued that if MAFF had only adopted a programme of mass vaccination the whole epidemic could and would have been brought under control within a matter of days. He was scathing about MAFF's handling of the situation and said it should be called 'The Ministry of Death'.

Like many others, I stayed behind after the meeting to join the group. It was heartening for me to meet other like-minded people who were equally determined to make a stand and fight for their animals. Names, addresses and telephone numbers were exchanged, should any of us need help in the event of MAFF arriving to demand entry to kill our healthy stock. I returned home, feeling much less alone than I had a few hours earlier.

Next morning I went off to the local DIY store and purchased some padlocks and strong chains. I fitted these to both my gates of entry and felt much more secure when I had done so. Susan Bull arrived with a Union Jack and another flag bearing the skull and crossbones, together with some balloons and bunting. I had also acquired a reproduction of the mask from the film *Scream* and I mentioned to Susan that in the same shop there had been a comic head of Tony Blair, but that I could not afford to buy that as well. Susan's response was to head off and purchase it at once.

We decked out the front of the cottage with all that we had collected, almost as if we were preparing for the celebration of a royal jubilee. I say almost because the skull and crossbones would hardly be considered appropriate for a royal celebration, unless of course one was a republican, which I am not.

Finally, so that no one could be in any doubt of my intentions, I placed across the entrance of my drive a 'road closed' board of red and white vertical stripes, which had been left behind years ago by the gas board, on which were just enough white spaces for me to write in capital letters: 'M A F F   O F F   M Y   S H E E P'.

While we were doing all this, the first lorry loads of live healthy sheep taken from within three kilometre zones were being delivered to Great Orton for slaughter and burial. If vaccination was going to come, it was already going to be too late for some. Would it be too late for me?

I had barricaded myself behind chained gates. If MAFF and the Army wanted to have a fight, I was ready for them.

7

TACKLING MAFF

While I was preparing myself for battle, I received devastating news from just across the border in Scotland, where the culling policy seemed to have been prosecuted altogether more vigorously and to have been met with much less resistance than in Cumbria. Susan Bryden and her father Andrew Taylor, who lived in Lockerbie and from whose champion flock I had acquired Mr Universe, had had all of their Ryelands 'taken out', which was the euphemistic description now being used generally in place of 'shot'.

Foot and mouth had moved north from Longtown market to the Lockerbie area courtesy of the local dealers until the smoke and flames of the funeral pyres were barely a kilometre from their smallholding. The inevitable letter had followed, informing Susan and Andrew that they were within a three-kilometre zone and that their sheep would therefore have to be culled within a week.

Susan Bryden had written immediately to MAFF headquarters in Edinburgh, requesting that special consideration be given to their sheep on the grounds of the Ryelands' rare breed status. But, before any reply had been received, they had been telephoned on a Sunday morning to be told that the cull was to go ahead at 1pm on the following day.

Monday had dawned grey and foreboding and by 1pm, when their cull was due to begin, various cars, lorries and loading shovels had congregated at their road end. However, instead of going to Susan's as notified, the assembled cavalcade had advanced on a neighbour, whose cull was not scheduled until 5pm.

As a result, Susan and her father had first to endure the sights and sounds of three groups of neighbours' sheep being 'taken out', including eighty lambs, the eldest of which were not more than three weeks old and the youngest of which had been born within the last twenty four hours. Only then was it the turn of the 'Broomwell' Ryeland Flock.

Susan's father had penned their sixteen adult sheep and eight lambs in the yard and, Ryelands being the docile creatures that they are, they had stood or sat patiently during that long afternoon awaiting their fate.

When the end came, it was very quick. The lady vet and her squad dispatched the sheep by firing a bolt into each head and the lambs by lethal injection. Then the lifeless bodies were transported by loading shovel to a large sealed container truck at the end of the road. From there they were removed to a rendering plant so that at least Susan and her father, both of whom had gone indoors while these final acts were taking place, were spared the awfulness of a burning pit for their beloved sheep.

The Broomwell Flock had been established in 1982 and had produced several breed champions at the major shows in Scotland and in the north of England. The Broomwell name was renowned throughout the community of Ryeland breeders. Now, on one afternoon, the Broomwell Flock had been wiped out. Nearly twenty years of breeding, rearing and showing rare breed sheep had been terminated in barely twenty minutes.

How long would it be before my flock went the same way?

After hearing this news, I decided that I had to step up a gear in my campaign and I wrote a letter to Prince Charles, who was after all the patron of the Rare Breeds Survival Trust. I thought that I might grab the attention of His Royal Highness by mentioning the fact that his ancestor, King George III had kept a pure bred Ryeland flock at Windsor.

Apparently, Farmer George, as he was nicknamed, had been particularly appreciative that, because of their short, stocky legs, the Ryelands could be let loose to graze in the royal orchards without him having to worry that they would strip the trees of apples or any other fruit. I reflected that George III would have been decidedly less appreciative if the ancestors of Topsy and Fiver had accompanied his Ryelands.

Two days later I received a telephone call from St James's Palace. It was the Prince's assistant private secretary, Elizabeth Buchanan. At first I thought that it was someone playing a joke on me but I soon realised that she really was who she said she was. I must admit that I did break down in tears because she was so sympathetic to my plight and wanted to know exactly what was going on in the area. I explained that Cumbria's sheep population was being decimated and that all we had was empty fields for miles and miles. Elizabeth said I should not hesitate to contact her if ever I needed to talk to someone, no matter what time of day or night.

Various action groups were being formed against the culling of healthy livestock. One such group was known as Save Animal Deaths or SAD for short. Ellie Logan and Pat Fisher organised several demonstrations and I attended as many as I could locally. However, I could not and dared not go too far to attend these or stay for too long. What might have been happening back at home was always a worry.

Home indeed was attracting a fair degree of attention as a result of my Union Jack, skull and crossbones and Tony Blair effigy. Owen from the Press Association came to take some more photographs of me clutching a lamb, but this time flanked by my flags and a grinning Prime Minister. Three of Owen's pictures ended up on the Newsmakers' website alongside photographs of Brigadier Birtwistle and slaughtered sheep.

A neighbouring farmer called by to say that he was fixing a date for his sheep to be valued for financial compensation prior to having them culled. Would I like him to arrange for the valuer to call on me at the same time? I gestured towards my flags and the 'MAFF Off My Sheep' board and told him that I was not doing all this for fun. If my sheep contracted foot and mouth that was one thing. But they were not going to be culled otherwise, just because of this senseless policy on the part of the government.

New regulations meant that there could be no deliveries to any farms within 3 kilometre zones. I was desperate for hay and straw and I managed to persuade someone who had plenty of both and who had no animals to come by. He had to stop in the road so as not to come on to my land and pass the hay and straw across. There were a hundred bales of each and I was exhausted by the time I had finished carrying them into the shed but thankful to have restocked. Normally at this time all of the Ryelands would have been out on the grass and not locked inside a shed.

By now it was April and my Blackies, who were out in the adjoining field were beginning to lamb. I had been told to watch out for any ewe leaving the rest of the flock, as that would be a sure sign that she was about to lamb. It was then necessary to keep an eye on the ewe and, as soon as she had lambed, to try to reach the lamb as quickly as possible so as to dress the lamb's navel. I was told that, if I were lucky, the ewe would be busy having another lamb while I was doing this and so she would not run away and leave the first.

Sure enough I spotted a Blackie leaving the rest and in no time she had given birth and was licking her lamb. I ran across the field as fast as I could and picked up the lamb. The new mother moved away but not too far and, while I started to dress the lamb's navel, she gave birth to another. I grabbed the second lamb to do the same thing, while she went back to the first lamb to find out what I had been doing to it. When I had finished with the second, I walked away and she carried out another inspection.

A few minutes later, I realised that another two ewes were lambing at the same time. My instructions had not covered what to do when presented with this situation. I managed to sort out one lamb and then went to see to the other, which was at the other end of the field with its mother. As I approached, the ewe saw me and started to run. And when I say run I mean run. But what was amazing was that the newly born lamb started running as well and, what is more, ran every bit as fast as its mother. I could not believe my eyes and it was with some difficulty, aided by my shepherd's crook that I managed at long last to catch it.

My youngest son Andrew, now in his early twenties and back in Newcastle from London, had come across in order to give me some support for a couple of days. Like all the rest of my family, Andrew knew nothing about farming or livestock and had no ambition to follow in his mother's footsteps. But I was grateful for some company and a second pair of hands.

He came over on the train and I collected him at Wetheral station en route for a demonstration outside MAFF's head office at Rosehill, on the edge of Carlisle, where Ellie Logan was presenting a petition against the culling of healthy animals. Andrew agreed to come along only on condition that I did not shout out any abuse or otherwise cause a disturbance. We parked the car some way from MAFF's offices and started to walk towards the other protesters. I was dressed completely in black and had donned my *Scream* mask, so that my face was completely covered. I was carrying a Shaun the Sheep back pack and a placard bearing the words 'Stop Slaughtering Our Flocks. Vaccinate. Vaccinate. Vaccinate.' Andrew followed at a distance, which lengthened the nearer I got to the protesters.

'Hello Moira!' shouted out one of the photographers, as I approached. So much for my cunning disguise! Andrew took refuge behind a lamppost.

MAFF sent someone out to collect the petition. Andrew asked for the keys so that he could go back to sit in the car until the whole embarrassing scene was over.

The next day I needed to nip out to the shops and asked him if he would stay out in the field to keep an eye on two Blackies who were in the second stage of lambing and, in particular, ward off the crows that were circling the sheep. Crows can be a problem on two counts with newly born lambs. First, they have a liking for the afterbirth and, secondly, they can descend and pluck out a lamb's eyes, particularly if the lamb is weak. Since the slaughter had started in Cumbria, crows seemed to have become noticeably more bloodthirsty with the number of dead carcasses lying around.

I left Andrew sitting on a deck chair in the field reading a skateboard magazine. When I came back only ten minutes later, he was no longer in the deck chair and was no longer reading. He was standing in the field, ashen faced, looking in horror at one of the ewes that had just lambed and from whom the afterbirth was coming away.

'Oh my God,' he shouted, 'I can't stand all this blood and guts. What time's the next train from Carlisle? I've just remembered I've got an urgent appointment.'

Andrew waited until I had grabbed hold of my terramycin antibiotic spray to dress the lamb's navel before heading back into the cottage. He declined my offer of lunch. 'I couldn't eat a thing,' he said, 'You must be mad - absolutely mad,' he added, shaking his head, 'Where's the train timetable?' He was gone within the hour.

Eventually all except one of the Blackies had lambed, but this last one seemed to be taking an age. It was some days later, while I was out in the field checking on the lambs, that I noticed that this last Blackie had lambed and was starting to lamb another. But the second had only got as far as its head and was having trouble getting any further. What should I do?

I decided that the first thing to try would be to get the Blackie into the shed. I managed to pick up her first lamb and started to walk backwards, as if I were retiring in the presence of royalty, carrying the lamb in my arms so that the ewe could see where it was. It helped that the lamb began to cry for her and slowly she began to follow, as I gradually made my way across the field. After what seemed an eternity, I reached the shed and placed the lamb on the floor. I hid out of sight until the Blackie warily stepped inside to join her lamb and then I slammed the door shut behind her. At least I now had the Blackie trapped so that she could not run away from me.

While this had been going on, Susan Bull had stopped her car outside and was calling out at the gate, asking if I wanted anything from the shops. Remembering that she was a retired district nurse, I shouted back that I did not need anything from the shops but what I did need was some urgent help from a midwife. Susan came to the door to find out what was going on and by now I had managed to pen the ewe and her first lamb into a small part of the shed.

'Susan,' I said, 'If I hang on to this bloody ewe's horns, can you try and pull out this lamb that's got stuck?'

'Moira,' replied Susan, in her best district nurse voice, 'you will have to wait for the contractions.'

'To hell with the contractions!' I yelled back, in most un-district nurse tones, 'this lamb isn't going to get out any further on its own. We have to save it. Grab hold and when I say pull - pull!'

By now, as well as the lamb's head, one shoulder was sticking out, but the other leg was tucked back on itself and well and truly stuck.

What a job. I hung onto the Blackie's horns, with some difficulty because both my hands were covered in lambing oil, as if it was the last thing that I was ever going to do, and prayed that Susan could manage to pull out the lamb. She had to hold the poor lamb's foot and push the head back, while getting the other leg to straighten before the head could then re-appear in the correct lambing fashion. At last she had done it and was walking in front of me, proudly holding out the lamb as if it were a new born baby and I were the mother.

I was still hanging onto the ewe's horns and told her to put the lamb down on the ground in front of the ewe. Susan did so, muttering that if she had ever delivered a baby in such a way during her professional career she would have been struck off. The ewe began licking the second lamb. Susan and I made for the cottage and a stiff drink.

One interesting result of this episode was that this particular Blackie lost her fear of me and, after she had returned to the field with her two lambs, she did not follow the others in running away when I came out to visit them.

The lambing of the Blackies was a welcome distraction from the horrors that were happening beyond the confines of Ryeland Cottage. Having raised hopes that vaccination might be introduced as a means of combating foot and mouth, the government announced that plans for 'ring vaccination' of animals close to outbreaks of disease had been postponed because it was believed that the slaughter policy was now working.

Day after day, television and newspapers relayed heart-rending pictures and stories as the culling continued and day after day, I seemed to spend hours looking at each ewe and each lamb for any possible signs of foot and mouth. At the end of each day I thanked God that I was still safe from the disease. But even so, I knew it was only a matter of time before I heard something from MAFF regarding my presence within a three-kilometre zone.

In fact, when the letter that I had been dreading finally arrived in the post, it came not from MAFF but from the local auctioneers, Harrison & Hetherington. They informed me that I was now in a three kilometre zone and would I telephone to make arrangements to have my sheep valued prior to slaughter. I was allowed to choose between having them shot on my premises or collected and taken to Great Orton.

My reaction was one of panic. I read that letter over and over again and then ran out to the shed and my Ryelands. They all looked so peaceful. Lambs were charging backwards and forwards from one end of the shed to the other, while mothers sat watching and chewing their cud. I burst into tears. How could I allow such healthy sheep to be shot and burned? It was sheer madness.

My tears soon turned to anger and, having Irish blood, I do have a temper to be reckoned with! I telephoned a friend in Yorkshire whom I had got to know from attending the agricultural shows and whose sheep were well out of range from foot and mouth. Sandie suggested that I ring Pat Walker of the North Yorkshire Smallholders, because she was up to date with all the relevant legal procedures.

Since I was not a member, I did not think that she would entertain me but I could not have been more wrong. Pat listened patiently to my outpourings and calmed me down. She told me that the former publisher and millionaire Peter Kindersley, who now had an organic farm known as Sheepdrove, had struck a deal with a leading firm of solicitors, Burges

Salmon, who specialised in agricultural law. Under this arrangement, Burges Salmon would act for any farmer or smallholder, who was fighting to save their stock, at a cost to that person of only £250 plus VAT, with Peter Kindersley meeting any additional costs.

Pat gave me the telephone number for Burges Salmon and also gave me a lot of other good advice and names of people to contact. One in particular was Jane Barribal of Farmtalking. Jane was a former veterinary nurse who had set up a help line on the internet and had telephones manned 24 hours a day to give advice to farmers and smallholders. She had put together help packs setting out their rights in the face of the action being taken by MAFF.

At this time I did not have so much as a computer, never mind access to the internet and I realised that I was missing out on a huge amount of information that was in circulation from all manner of sources about foot and mouth and what was happening in different parts of the country. I did however acquire a second hand fax machine and soon friends, particularly Pat Walker, were downloading information from their computers and faxing page after page across to me.

At times my living room looked as if it had been over run by gigantic paper snakes. Chloe the dachshund certainly thought so. First she would bark at the fax machine as it started to churn out the paper. Then she would attack the paper itself as it advanced across the floor and start tearing it up if I did not manage to get there before her. On more than one occasion I had to telephone the sender and ask if they could retransmit one or more pages that had been through my dog shredder.

Although I had the telephone number for Burges Salmon, who turned out to be based in Bristol, at the other end of the country, the letter from Harrison & Hetherington had arrived on a Saturday. Bearing in mind that Susan Bryden had been telephoned by MAFF on a Sunday and given 24 hours notice of her cull, I did not fancy taking any chances and leaving things until Monday. What should I do in the meantime to protect my position?

I telephoned a local councillor and friend, Doreen Parsons, and she gave me the home number of David Maclean, MP for Penrith and the Borders, who had attracted a high profile in speaking out for Cumbrian farmers. I spoke to David and apologised for troubling him at a weekend, but he was most supportive and gave me the wording to use for a written appeal to MAFF against the culling of my healthy flock. Having written out my letter of appeal to MAFF and another letter to Harrison & Hetherington, to the effect that I did not require their services, as I would be making other arrangements, I drove the short distance to Rosehill and posted each letter through the relevant letterbox.

I was not alone in lodging an appeal to MAFF and co-incidentally that weekend Nick Brown was interviewed on the BBC's Sunday morning show *Breakfast with Frost*, complaining that the number of appeals being made was endangering the entire foot and mouth policy by delaying still further the gap between outbreaks and slaughter. 'People want to argue about it,' he told Sir David Frost, 'But the truth is the animals do have to go, otherwise the disease will remorselessly spread.'

I most certainly did want to argue about it. A clip of a television interview I had done with the BBC a little earlier was broadcast on Sunday evening's national news bulletin. There I was proclaiming, 'Quite honestly, if they take my sheep to Great Orton, they can take me and shoot me as well.'

On the Monday I was contacted by BBC Radio 4 and found myself being interviewed that lunchtime on *The World at One* by Nick Clarke. I explained that the main aim of my appeal was to play for time in the hope that if I and other appellants held out long enough, MAFF would be forced to vaccinate. My interview was followed by one with Ellie Logan of Stop Animal Deaths, who said that the government did not have a right of access to land that would allow them to cull livestock if people barred their access.

Then, I suppose to provide BBC balance to the argument, a lawyer came on to say that, while people did indeed have the right to refuse access to their land if the people entering did not have legal authority, nevertheless the 1981 Animal Health Act could be used to provide a legal basis for entering private land. Finally, a lecturer in Farm Animal Medicine from Glasgow University said that, in his view, MAFF was right to urge farmers not to appeal against the cull of apparently healthy animals. My God, I thought, if that was typical of the thinking in Scotland, no wonder Susan Bryden's attempt to save her Ryelands had come to nothing.

As for the legal position, I had already that Monday telephoned Burges Salmon and explained my predicament to one of their associates, Simon

Leach, who agreed to take on my case.

In the next few days, my second hand fax machine was working over-time as I faxed as much information as possible to Simon and he faxed back drafts of a proposed letter to MAFF. The final version, which went to MAFF read as follows:

'We have received instructions to act on behalf of Mrs Moira Linaker. We understand from our client that you are considering the cull of her sheep as they fall within 3 kilometres of a confirmed infection at Warwick Holme Gate Farm, which was confirmed on 20th March. Our client received a letter on Saturday 7 April from Harrison & Hetherington Ltd informing her that her holding fell within 3 kilometres of a confirmed case. Our client informs us that Warwick Holme Farm is approximately 2.5 kilometres from her holding.

'On 8 April our client wrote to you appealing against the proposed cull of her stock and a copy of that letter is enclosed.

'The provisions of the Foot & Mouth Disease Order 1983 state that the Veterinary Officer may enter our client's farm and take samples to ascertain whether the disease exists. Our client has inspected her flock of sheep regularly and those inspections have revealed no evidence of infection. Further, we understand that you have not inspected our client's sheep or taken samples. Our client has no objections to those inspections or samples being taken.

'We understand that the slaughter of sheep on premises within 3 kilometres of an infected premises in the area is the 'third stage' slaughter policy being adopted and is based on the belief that the sheep have been exposed to the risk of FMD infection and that disease, where there are no cattle or pigs on the premises will, in most cases, not be apparent to the owner.

'Below we have listed the factors which our client thinks you should take into account in considering whether or not to slaughter her sheep and, given those factors, our client does not believe that you would have reasonable grounds for ordering the slaughter of her sheep. For ease of reference, we shall use numbered paragraphs:

'1) As we have already explained, our client's holding is approximately 2.5 kilometres from the infected premises. Our client's sheep have not been off her holding in the last 5 years apart from attendance at shows in the last 2 years.

'2) Our client's sheep consist of a flock of 15 Ryelands, which is a rare breed, and 14 crosses.

'3) Before the current outbreak of FMD, there were only 3,000 Ryelands in the country. As explained in our client's letter to you dated 8 April, she has a blood line which she is desperate to keep. In particular, our client has two rams, one of which may be the last of a particularly rare blood line. This ram has an extra rib and therefore is unusually long and our client believes this is a rare animal in what is already a rare breed. Further, both rams have been housed since January and have not been in contact with the ewes.

'4) The ram in question was purchased from a Mrs Susan Bryden, the owner of the Broomwell Flock in Lockerbie but we understand from our client that this flock was culled some 2 weeks ago.

'5) As we understand your 'third stage' slaughter policy, the first priority is to slaughter sheep within one kilometre of the infected premises. The second priority is to destroy sheep within 3 kilometres of the infected premises but the general principle may be varied given serological results which should indicate areas of greater or lesser risk.

'6) The Minister has already given a commitment to preserving rare breeds and valuable genetic material. Given our client's opposition to her flock being culled, and as we understand the guidance, in these particular circumstances, you should collect sufficient blood samples for testing to give you a very high degree of confidence of detecting a very low level of prevalence of infection.

'7) Our client is quite prepared to allow you to inspect and test her flock and, if necessary, arrangements can be made for our client's own vet to inspect the flock and explain its value and why it should be exempted from the cull.

'8) Apart from the above, Warwick Holme Farm was listed as a confirmed case on 20 March. Some three weeks have now elapsed since the slaughter of the stock on that farm. The Chief Vet accepts that the incubation period is between 2 and 14 days and, as we are now passed the incubation period, this reinforces our client's belief that the appropriate course is to test and monitor her flock and not proceed with a cull.

'9) There have been no livestock movements off the holding since last July and there has been the absolute minimum of human movement off the holding.

'If despite the above, you believe that there are good reasons why the slaughter of our client's livestock falls within paragraph 3 Schedule 3 of the Animal Health Act 1981, please specify those reasons, confirming the investigations that you have undertaken to justify your decision.

'You should not order the slaughter of our client's flock before you have provided that information in order to give our client the opportunity to provide a further response.

'If you are able to demonstrate good grounds for ordering the slaughter of our client's flock, which, for the reasons given above, our client does not accept, then our client's position is one in which vaccination should be used instead. Therefore, our client would be prepared to agree to vaccination as an alternative to slaughter, subject to clarification and agreement as to the conditions which would then apply.

'Finally, if, despite all the above, our client's flock is slaughtered, please note that her flock have significant value over and above their pure current market value because she has a pedigree flock, as explained and as a result, the slaughter of our client's flock will cause her significant further financial loss.

'We appreciate that at the moment it is likely to be extremely difficult for you to respond in writing. However, before you visit our client's farm and, in particular, take any steps towards culling her flock, please telephone the writer to discuss further.'

I was very pleased with this letter, in particular with the comment at paragraph 8 about Warwick Holme Farm and the period that had elapsed since confirmation of the outbreak there, which point had been suggested to me by Pat Walker. I drew comfort too from the fact that, during the subsequent three weeks, there had been no more confirmed cases within three kilometres of Warwick Bridge, despite the fact that over this same period the number of confirmed foot and mouth cases in Cumbria had increased from just over 200 to nearly 550.

Burges Salmon's letter went to MAFF just before the Easter weekend and I felt confident that it would buy me some more time, so long as my sheep managed to remain free of infection. All the while I was carrying on with my daily checks and continuing to ensure that all my sheep had their regular dosage of Borax and grapefruit pip extract, the former now coming from Crossgates Homeopathic in North Yorkshire, the latter still being sent me by Christina from Newcastle. I did not know if this treatment was making any difference but at least I felt that I was doing something to help my sheep.

Would there be a change of policy by MAFF that might help them and me even more?

8

AN EASTER PROMISE

That year the message of Easter seemed particularly poignant. Jesus, the Lamb of God, had suffered on the cross for the sins of mankind and here in Cumbria real life lambs were suffering for the sins of some farmers, some dealers and, so far as I was concerned, some ministers and their officials. But whereas Jesus had risen again from the dead in just three days, there was no prospect of an imminent resurrection in the Cumbrian countryside. By the weekend the numbers of animals reported killed in Cumbria because of foot and mouth had reached 600,000 and of those more than 500,000 were sheep.

On Easter Monday, the government's chief scientific adviser, Professor David King, visited Carlisle to meet with farmers' leaders. It was now only two weeks before a quarter of a million beef and dairy cattle would be moving out of their winter quarters and into open fields and the proposal was that these cattle should be vaccinated against foot and mouth. Sheep, I noticed from the press reports, were not included in the vaccination programme. Nevertheless it was a start.

However, to my dismay, it was clear that the government was not prepared to proceed with this limited programme of inoculation without securing the co-operation of farmers and that this was unlikely to be forthcoming. Only the week before, it was reported that David Maclean had surveyed 240 local farmers on the subject of vaccination and had had eighty per cent of these respond positively. Now, many farmers, particularly pedigree specialists, seemed to be against the idea, fearing that nobody would want to buy milk or meat from vaccinated livestock and that the government would not compensate them for any losses incurred as a result.

By the end of that week, after three days of talks with Professor King, Ben Gill, the president of the National Farmers Union, declared that vaccination would be a 'massive gamble' and that the current policy of culling was working.

'The battle against foot and mouth is being won - that's clear from the reduction in outbreaks,' he asserted, 'the scientific arguments alone are not clear cut. Aside from our fears that vaccination would prolong the outbreak and result in more culling long term, we have still not received adequate assurances there would be a market for products from vaccinated animals.'

As so often during the foot and mouth epidemic, I was moved to despair and then anger. I had smallholders' membership of the NFU and here was the president effectively putting a block on a humane initiative, which could help put a stop to the dreadful carnage that we had witnessed in the last few weeks, in favour of continuing with a policy that I regarded as barbaric in its approach and indiscriminate in its application.

In a fury, I cut up my NFU member's card, put the bits in an envelope and posted it to the local NFU office. I had little enough money as it was and I was not going to waste any more on this outfit. With friends like these, I thought, who needs enemies?

'The scientific arguments alone are not clear cut.' What was so scientific about culling every single sheep within a range of three kilometres, I wanted to know? Always assuming of course that MAFF could find the right three kilometres to start with. There had been at least one report that, owing to a map grid reference error, a slaughter team from MAFF had quite unnecessarily killed three hundred lambs and two hundred ewes, when they should have been on a farm miles - I am sorry, that should be kilometres - away. The farmers, a husband and wife, had told the slaughter team that their farm did not lie within a culling zone, but they would not listen and had carried on.

MAFF had apologised to the farming couple and were reported in the local *News & Star* as saying that slaughter teams would soon be given 'global positioning systems to prevent future errors.'

What on earth did they mean by 'global positioning systems' I wondered. I had visions of a MAFF official zooming into outer space to take satellite photographs and beam them back to Mission Control, Rosehill, following which a MAFF team would be dispatched to the other end of the world to inform a bemused sheep farmer in New Zealand that his whole flock would have to be taken out. Except that, assuming the average build of a New Zealand sheep farmer to be that of an All Blacks rugby forward, I thought it more likely that any taking out would be performed by the farmer on MAFF than vice versa.

The incompetence of MAFF seemed to know no bounds. In response to my appeal, MAFF telephoned to say that they would like to send one of their vets to take some blood samples. I said that I was not going to allow any vet, who might have been on infected premises, to set foot on my smallholding. However, I knew that my own vet, Jonathan Lomax of Craig Robinson, had not been on any such farms and I was quite willing to let him take blood samples from my sheep. I telephoned Jonathan and asked him about this.

'Moira,' he replied, 'I will happily take some samples. But MAFF has not issued any guidance to vets in practice. I don't know how many samples to take, how many sheep to take samples from, where on the sheep I am supposed to take the samples and where and how I am supposed to send the samples that I have taken!'

'Well,' I said, 'can you write me a letter in the meantime confirming that I have been in touch with you about blood samples, just in case someone from MAFF turns up at my gates to do anything to the sheep.'

'Not a problem,' said Jonathan, 'I'll do that. Then I'll go upstairs and speak to MAFF.'

His practice and the MAFF office were in the same building. Jonathan was as good as his word and faxed me a letter on his headed stationery confirming that I had been in touch with him about blood samples for my pedigree sheep and that he had advised me to wait, pending clarification from MAFF on the details of the scheme.

Yet again, I was not taking any chances, because it had been reported in the press that MAFF officials were going to get tough with farmers who were refusing to co-operate with the 'voluntary' three kilometre cull. Out of 1,600 farmers, 240 had apparently refused and I assumed that I was counted in as one of the latter.

I was continuing to receive press coverage about my situation. Just before Easter, for example, the *Daily Express* had published a photograph of me cuddling up to some of my Ryelands with the caption, 'Chain Reaction: Moira Lineker has locked her farm's gates to keep out the slaughtermen.'

I was amused at the misspelling of my name, which is not uncommon. If I had a five pound note for every time someone has asked me if I were related to the England footballer, Gary Lineker, I would have been able

The Cottage and its original animal residents, middle, Chloe the Dachshund and bottom, Holly the Doberman/ Rhodesian Ridgeback cross.

Left, Moira's first sheep from the lamb bank feeding at the milk bar.

Centre, Moira's first lamb shed!

Bottom, the geese with the ungentle-manly gander in the middle.

Left, Fiver having her oil treatment to try and get her fleece to grow. She's still alive and happy in 2004.

Below, Topsy giving Moira her morning lick, just like a dog!

Left, training for the shows - who's next for the halter?

Below, the first Ryelands registered as Moira's Eden Flock - Mr Universe centre stage as ever.

Left, Mr Universe displays his first and Titan's second prize rosettes from the Royal Lancashire Show, 2000.

Above, A collage of photographs of Stephen taken shortly before his death.

Above, Ryeland Cottage during the FMD crisis in 2001 and below, Harry and Amanda Jane, Behind Chained Gates - but Highgrove-bound ultimately.

Moira at the commemorative tree planting ceremony at Rosehill, Carlisle, 26 March 2002. A weeping willow seemed appropriate.

Below left, Susan Bull, Moira's staunchest ally during the FMD campaign, courtesy of the News & Star.

This tree was planted as a symbol of hope, a sign of new life, firmly planted for the future for all those who suffered during this 2001 Foot & Mouth epidemic

Right, Moira with Fiver's 16 pound lamb at one hour old. The smaller lamb is a normal sized week old lamb. Photograph courtesy of the Cumberland News.

Below, picture of Mr Universe and Moira before the Royal Highland Show in 2003 courtesy of the Newcastle Journal.

FMD survivor shows where there's wool there's a way

Mr Universe has world at his feet

SHOW OFF:
Prize ram Mr
Universe with
Moira
Linton.

By Anna Lognonné

(0191) 201 6243
anna.lognonne@ncjmedia.co.uk

HE symbolised hope during the darkest hours of the foot-and-mouth epidemic.

Now Mr Universe is to take part in one of the UK's most prestigious shows, thanks to *The Journal*.

Fears for the threatened Ryeland ram highlighted the plight of Cumbrian sheep farmers fighting Government animal-culling plans.

Against the odds he survived and now he is to take part in the four-day Royal Highland Show, which takes place on the outskirts of Edinburgh from June 19.

But it is an expensive business.

80

to give up playing the Lottery years ago.

I was also amused at the *Express* article referring to me as a 'sheep farmer' when of course I was only a smallholder. This was a common mistake made in press reports. One of my favourite examples was sent to me from the USA by Sandra Rudd, who I had never met but who I now know as Sandie and hope to meet one day. She had been moved to write, having seen the photograph of me in my woolly hat clutching the Ryeland lamb reproduced in the *Seattle Post Intelligencer* under the headline 'British Farmer Holds On'.

She sellotaped the photograph and the brief report underneath it, which mentioned Warwick Bridge, to a US airmail envelope and posted it from Seattle. The Royal Mail delivered it a few days later. I reflected that perhaps the Royal Mail should have been assisting MAFF with their 'global positioning systems.'

I had given the lamb in that much reproduced photograph the pet name of Harry. He appeared to be destined for a fame that might rival, if not eclipse, that of Mr Universe.

First, I heard again from Shireen, the artist who had written asking permission to do a painting based on the photograph of Harry and me for the Royal Academy of Art summer school exhibition. She wrote to tell me that her painting had been accepted. Harry and I were to be exhibited to thousands of visitors in London. Pleased as I was by this news, I have to admit that I was less than cheered by the title, which Shireen had chosen for the painting. She had called it 'Doom'.

Secondly, I heard again from the office of the Prince of Wales, only this time it was a letter from Prince Charles personally rather than his assistant private secretary. I had told the Prince, when first writing to him, that his ancestor, King George III, under the influence of his agricultural adviser, Joseph Banks, had kept a flock of Ryelands at Windsor. I had then suggested that it would be nice if Ryelands were re-introduced, as it were, to the royal family. If I managed to get through this crisis with my flock intact, I said that I would happily give him a ram lamb and ewe lamb from my flock to enable him to start his own Ryeland flock. The ram lamb that I had earmarked for this honour was Harry. I enclosed some photographs of the Ryelands.

Prince Charles had written back to say that he was most touched by my offer and thought that the Ryelands looked wonderful in the photographs.

He had a growing collection of rare breed sheep, in his capacity as patron of the Rare Breeds Survival Trust, but felt it best to wait and see how the next few weeks went before making any decisions. In the meantime, he prayed with all his heart that I would be spared the scourge of this awful disease.

The Prince's letter was a real tonic to my frame of mind, which often sank to the depths of depression, as day after day I waited and wondered what would happen. In the weeks to come I was to receive constant support from his private office and I am sure that I was not the only one, judging from the interest which the Prince showed in visiting Cumbria over the next few months.

I was also heartened that, despite the NFU national leadership's opposition to vaccination, the issue was still being debated and that calls were being made for vaccination to be extended to sheep. The Cumbria foot and mouth task force was reported to have pleaded with the Prime Minister to go ahead with the vaccination of Cumbria's fell sheep as soon as possible.

There was particular concern for the so-called hefted flocks under threat, the Rough Fell, the Swaledale and the Herdwick. The loss of these sheep breeds would be truly irreplaceable because their survival in the areas which they inhabit is entirely dependent on the knowledge passed down from one generation of sheep to the next. Each ewe teaches her lamb where to go and where not to go and so on. If these sheep were to be wiped out in a cull, it was not a case of re-stocking after the all clear had been sounded. The sheep would have gone for good and the landscape of the Lake District would be changed irrevocably.

One of my new friends through Farmers for Action, Suzanne Greenhill from Cockermouth, was particularly vocal on behalf of the Lakeland Herdwicks. She was also adept at finding out information from a variety of sources about what was happening across the country in response to foot and mouth and through her I obtained fax numbers of ministers, MPs, peers and MEPs. I was soon sending faxes left, right and centre, appealing for the introduction of vaccination in general and the protection of rare breeds in particular.

As April came to an end, I heard on Radio Cumbria that the Prime Minister was paying what would be his second visit to Carlisle in five weeks. He was coming, it was said, to pay tribute to Brigadier Birtwistle on his retirement from the Army and, more particularly, on his retirement from sorting out the mess, which he had been asked to deal with during Tony Blair's previous visit.

Brigadier 'Birtie' should have retired from the Army at the beginning of April but he had agreed to stay on and help tackle the foot and mouth crisis in Cumbria. In a matter of days he had brought order where there had been chaos, inspired confidence where there had been despair and had done so with an appealing mixture of toughness and compassion. Much was made of the fact that as well as being a soldier he was a Cambridge graduate in English Literature. But in fact it was probably of more relevance that he came from the North West, that he was clearly an avid countryman (he admitted that he had originally wanted to be a farmer himself) and that he was a natural diplomat.

I was not surprised that the Prime Minister wanted to come and pay homage. Locally, the Brigadier had dug a large hole at Great Orton and filled it with half a million dead sheep. Nationally, he had helped to dig the government and MAFF out of a far larger hole at Westminster.

Because Brigadier 'Birtie' had based his operational headquarters at Rosehill, I assumed that the Prime Minister would be meeting the Brigadier at the Shepherds Inn. I contacted Susan Bull and together we set off to give Mr Blair a welcome. On the way there, I was called on my mobile and told that he was not after all going to the Shepherds Inn but was instead heading for a hotel outside Carlisle.

'He'll be going to Dalston Hall,' said Susan immediately.

'How do you know that?' I asked.

'Gut feeling,' she replied, 'It's a bit out of the way.'

I did not have a clue where Dalston Hall was but Susan gave me directions. As we approached, I noticed a policeman standing at the entrance.

'Susan,' I said, 'he's not going to let us drive in there.'

'I've been to Dalston Hall. It's a long walk up that drive. Pull into the side and leave this to me.'

I parked the car. Susan got out and marched across to the policeman. Now, you have to bear in mind that Susan's father was in the Royal Marines and that she herself trained as a nurse with the Royal Navy. She could put on the style when the occasion demanded.

'Good day to you, officer,' said Susan, in a suitably authoritative voice, 'are you expecting the Prime Minister?'

'Yes, madam,' replied the policeman.

'Ah,' said Susan, 'very good. We've come to welcome him. Where can we park?'

'Oh,' said the policeman, 'just go straight up the drive and park at the end.'

'Thank you very much,' said Susan and returned towards the car. 'Drive on, Moira,' she commanded, as she climbed on board.

As we neared the hotel, we were greeted by the sound of cheers and applause. Other veterans of previous Rosehill protests had arrived before us and had been marshalled at one end by the police. Yet again I was dressed in black and I donned my trademark *Scream* mask, as soon as I got out of the car. Cries of 'Hello, Moira!' came from the assembled press and photographers as they caught sight of me with my Shaun the Sheep bag.

'Are you going to surge?' shouted one of the reporters.

'Of course we're going to surge,' shouted back Nick Green.

Nick is a climbing and mountaineering instructor from Keswick. Like so many others in Cumbria, his livelihood had been dramatically affected by the outbreak of foot and mouth and the way it had been handled. Nick has a voice like a megaphone. Indeed, I suspect you would think twice about following Nick up a mountain for fear that a shout from him would set off an avalanche.

The Prime Minister's car arrived and revved up as the driver spotted the crowd of protesters surging forward.

'We want some answers to some questions, Mr Blair,' shouted Nick, as the car swept past. 'Will you please come and talk to us, Mr Blair?'

An hour and a half later the Prime Minister came out but only to talk to the press and the cameras, not to us. We were kept behind a hedge, although we did our best to provide a background accompaniment to Mr Blair's press conference.

Only later did I discover that, apart from praising Brigadier Birtwistle, the Prime Minister had been explaining to farmers' leaders, vets and MAFF officials that the rules regarding the three kilometre culls were to be relaxed. There was much cynical comment that this was connected with the case of Phoenix the calf, whose story had dominated the national news the day before. Phoenix had somehow survived a pre-emptive cull on a Devon farm and had been spared. It was also suggested that, having had to abandon plans for a General Election on 1 May, the government was now looking towards an election in June and wanted to reduce the level of culling well before then.

Nonetheless, the fact was that from now on, where an outbreak of foot and mouth was confirmed on one farm, cattle on neighbouring farms within the three kilometre zones would no longer be culled automatically. MAFF vets would be allowed to decide each case on its merits. It was also stated that this relaxation would apply to rare breed and hefted sheep. But a vaccination policy for Cumbria, Nick Brown was reported to have said, was impractical without the support of a substantial majority of farmers, which was 'simply not there.'

There was talk of friction among farmers who had recently had uninfected cattle culled, which might have been saved had this amended policy been in force earlier. My thoughts turned to other smallholders who had already lost their rare breed sheep.

On the same day that the *Cumberland News* reported the Prime Minister's visit to Dalston Hall and the change of policy, the paper also published this letter from a smallholder in Wigton:

'My small flock of pedigree Shetland sheep were culled on Easter Sunday. They were a rare breed, very hardy with brilliant mothers that never gave any problems in lambing. They all had names and personalities. I knew them as individuals.'

If one substituted Ryeland for Shetland, I thought, that letter could have been written by me. I thanked God that I had not had to write such a letter and I prayed that I would never have to.

9

THE ELECTION

Shortly after the announced change of policy, MAFF published a 'Joint Instruction to Regional Operations Directors and Divisional Veterinary Managers', which set out the detail of how this was to be implemented, and I received a copy in the post. Since this was an internal departmental document, some of the language was unsurprisingly pure civil service speak. For example, at paragraph 4 (ii), MAFF directors and managers were told that, 'Dangerous contacts (via known movements of animals, personnel, vehicles, equipment etc or potential airborne spread) should be culled in accordance with the latest standing instructions (currently Section X of Chapter 3 as amended by Emergency Instruction 2001/95/VEXDT).'

No change there then, I thought. However, in the following paragraph came confirmation of the specific relaxations to the three kilometre cull, in particular, 'a strictly limited exception, following consultation on published proposals and summarised in paragraph 9 below, for rare breed sheep.'

My eyes skipped to the all-important paragraph 9, which read, 'Even where there is some risk of infection, breeding flocks or parts of those flocks, of rare breeds of sheep of particular genetic merit may also be spared in the national interest, provided they can be isolated from other susceptible livestock and managed in compliance with tight biosecurity. Separate guidance on this will be issued.' Good news, I thought. The final sentence of paragraph 9 was not such good news. 'Other sheep in such flocks, such as fat lambs and non-rare breeds, should be culled.'

From this, it would appear that the Ryeland flock, which I had kept segregated from the other sheep, would have a fighting chance of a reprieve, but that my non-rare breed sheep, Topsy, Fiver, the Blackies and all their lambs were still doomed.

I faxed the document through to Simon Leach at Burges Salmon. His view was that, at present, there was little point in doing anything further until MAFF had responded to my appeal and his letter of 12 April, much of which had in fact anticipated the changes now in force.

The 'separate guidance' mentioned in paragraph 9 of the Joint Instruction was issued by MAFF at the beginning of May. It applied to specific categories of sheep and goats as listed by the Rare Breeds Survival Trust. Ryelands were included in Category 7 and classified as a 'minority' breed, along with, for example, Hebridean and Shetland. The Trust's other categories were 'critical', 'endangered', 'vulnerable' and 'at risk', the latter including Southdown, a breed of sheep very similar in appearance to Ryelands.

The main point in the guidance was the provision for inspection and blood sampling of the rare breed sheep in question, to be followed by serological testing at the Animal Health Laboratory in Pirbright. Assuming the tests proved negative, the whole process was to be repeated fourteen days later. Simon Leach's letter to MAFF, on my behalf, had of course already stated that I had no objection to blood sampling of my sheep. Again, the advice from Simon was to wait and see.

On the same day that MAFF's 'separate guidance' came out Tony Blair held a press conference on the topic of foot and mouth. While there would be 'no complacency', Mr Blair claimed that the government's policy was working, as demonstrated by the continuing fall in the number of new daily cases.

'We are getting the disease under control,' he said. 'We have now all but completely cleared the backlog of animals waiting to be slaughtered... It is not over yet... but I believe we are on the home straight.'

Whether or not the Prime Minister was on the home straight for the defeat of foot and mouth, many political commentators were firmly of the view that he was on the home straight for calling a General Election. Originally, this had been expected for the beginning of May, but foot and mouth had put paid to that idea. Now, it seemed that the postponement need only be a short one and an election in early June was being forecast. In the circumstances it was most convenient that the battle against foot and mouth was finally being won.

That same day, seven new cases were confirmed in Cumbria, bringing the local total to 664 and the national total to 1,534.

A week later, I received a personal letter from the MAFF office at Rosehill. A month had elapsed since my letter of appeal and the follow up letter from my solicitor and this was the first communication from MAFF to acknowledge either. I presumed that the delay was at least partly because of what had been happening at the higher level of policy making over the last four weeks.

I was asked to provide written support to my appeal and an assessment from my own vet, which had to be carried out at my expense. The information required included:

❏ *Details of breed (only pedigree sheep/flocks are acceptable)*

❏ *A description of the sheep, goats or flocks to be exempted (eg a nucleus breeding unit, pet)*

❏ *Details of scrapie genotype if known. An applicant will not be refused entry on these grounds alone.*

❏ *Other scientific justification for exemption.*

❏ *A map and plan of the premises where the exempted sheep or goats are to be held.*

❏ *A formal written agreement that animals will be slaughtered if serological evidence of exposure to foot and mouth disease is found or if foot and mouth disease is confirmed in other animals on the premises.*

I was slightly puzzled at the repeated reference to goats. The letter was clearly addressed to me and referred to my appeal. My solicitor's letter had spelt out what sheep I had and had made no reference to goats. I wondered if someone from MAFF knew about Fiver, had assumed that she was a goat rather than a sheep and had decided that references to goats had better be included so as to be on the safe side.

The letter went on to set down various rules regarding premises and stock management. Having already confused me by including references to goats alongside sheep, the letter had now started referring to 'sheep, goats and camelid'. What on earth were camelid? The word was quite beyond me and quite beyond my *Collins Gem* dictionary. I had to telephone Susan Bull and ask her to consult her *Oxford English Dictionary*.

'Camelid, Moira,' Susan informed me, sounding rather like Owl in 'Winnie the Pooh' addressing a Bear of Very Little Brain, 'is the generic term which covers animals such as llamas and alpacas. In other words, llamas, alpacas and indeed camels, come to that, are all members of the camelid family.'

Goodness, I thought. Someone at MAFF really does know about Fiver and is covering all the possible angles to make sure she is not missed out.

The letter from MAFF concluded, 'Once the above information has been received and approved, we will arrange to serologically blood sample sheep, goats and camelid. Provided negative results are obtained, the flock/herd can then be temporarily registered.' I was requested to mark any correspondence to MAFF as '3KM cull exemptions.'

I faxed the letter to Simon Leach at Burges Salmon. It was a great comfort knowing that I had him and his firm at the end of a fax or mobile telephone in case of emergency. As ever, he was most helpful and calming when I subsequently spoke to him.

By now, the political commentators had been proved right and Tony Blair had called a General Election for 7 June. Almost at once it was noticeable how foot and mouth started to disappear from the national news coverage. I was concerned that, despite the change in policy and the acknowledgement of my appeal, I might still find myself the victim of precipitate action from MAFF, since all manner of stories were circulating of sudden visits by ministry officials to inspect and cull pet animals.

One or two stories were actually quite amusing. MAFF's resources had been so stretched by the crisis that they had had to call on the services of several vets from overseas. As a consequence, there were vets operating in Cumbria who came from the USA, Australia, New Zealand, South Africa, Italy, Spain, Sweden, Russia and so on. Whatever their degree of familiarity with foot and mouth, some of these vets were less than familiar with the English language. My own doctor, for example, told me that overseas vets had visited him not once but twice, on each occasion most concerned that he should permit them to examine his 'pigs', only for him to show them on each occasion that the 'pigs' in question were of the guinea pig variety.

But other stories were simply heartbreaking. One that particularly struck a chord concerned Carolyn Hoffe and her five pet Dutch Zwarbles sheep in Glasserton, which was across the border in Dumfries and Galloway. When foot and mouth had been confirmed within three kilometres of their paddock, she had brought the sheep into her cottage. Two days later, ministry vets, police and soldiers had forced their way into the cottage and slaughtered them. It was reported that shortly before the sheep were killed, one of them had knocked down a book from a shelf and it had fallen open. The sheep had looked down at the book, as if it were reading. The book was entitled *Vegetarian Cookery*.

I managed to get BBC *Look North* to do a piece on the television news to remind viewers, at least in the north of England, that the crisis had not gone away and that many farmers and smallholders were still under threat. The national ten o'clock news that day was full of the General Election campaign, including an extended feature on Charles Kennedy's first election as leader of the Liberal Democrats, and the opening of the Chelsea Flower Show, including film clips of the Queen, the Queen Mother, Princess Margaret and the Prince of Wales. Everything seemed reassuringly normal for the middle of May. Foot and mouth was not mentioned at all.

Then it was time to switch to the regional news and gratifyingly foot and mouth was the first item. I was filmed opening my letterbox at the end of my path and complaining about yet another letter from MAFF. Then I was shown feeding the Ryelands. Also featured was another smallholder, Ann Young from Great Salkeld, who was fighting to save her Merino sheep and who had also attracted quite a bit of media coverage during the outbreak.

Reporters and broadcasters were forever getting us muddled up. Perhaps it was the combination of Moira and Merino and the fact that both Ryelands and Merinos are very woolly that confused them. Often a reporter would turn up at Warwick Bridge and have to be redirected to Great Salkeld and vice versa. Ann was worse off than I was. At least I had my sheep right next to where I lived. Ann's were some way from where she lived and so she had had to move a caravan next to her sheep and stop there with them for the duration.

My main problem was the fact that I was getting low on hay for the Ryelands. Out in the large field, where roamed the Scotch Blacks, Topsy, Fiver and their lambs, there was an abundance of lush grass available. But because of the appeal and the biosecurity measures that had to be followed, I dared not let the Ryelands out into the field. I telephoned my usual supplier and asked if he could bring me some more hay and straw. He was very nervous about coming to my smallholding in the circumstances but eventually I managed to persuade him to visit and leave the hay and straw on the road, as he had done before.

I paid him by cheque and hoped the bank would not bounce this, since

I knew I was very much in the red, as a result of all the additional and unforeseen expenditure, which I had incurred since the outbreak of foot and mouth. I can honestly say that it never crossed my mind for a moment that I should give up the fight to save my animals and take the financial compensation that I would have undoubtedly been able to claim. Nevertheless it was a cruel irony that many farmers who had suffered the loss of their flocks and herds were compensated handsomely in monetary terms, in some cases far exceeding what they would have received had their animals lived, while those whose animals did survive suffered a double financial penalty. Their expenditure had increased while their income to meet that expenditure had not just decreased. It had vanished.

Despite all the support and encouragement, which I was receiving from various quarters, the strain and stress of the last few weeks were beginning to take their toll. I was having difficulty in eating and worked out that I had lost two stone in weight over the three months of March, April and May. I was having difficulty in sleeping and suffering recurring nightmares of men in white coats turning up at my gates and demanding entry. Every time the telephone rang, particularly in the evening, I was a bundle of nerves until I had discovered who was calling and established that it was not someone from MAFF at the other end of the line.

Following my appearance on *Tonight with Trevor MacDonald*, which now seemed years ago but in fact was less than two months earlier, Granada TV had given me a video camera and tapes so as to keep a daily diary. Each week a courier would arrive to collect my latest tape and deliver fresh tapes for recording. At first, I had found this helpful but after a while it had become something of a chore. I suspected too that possibly Granada might have been hoping that by now MAFF would have taken some action against my flock and they would have had some rivetting footage of my sheep being taken out, while I was dragged off by police and soldiers screaming and kicking.

My mood was not helped by the realisation that the first anniversary of Stephen's death was looming. I could hardly believe it was a year since his tragic and fatal accident. I tried to draw strength from imagining what he would have said to me, had he still been alive. 'Come on Mum. You're not one to give up. You can do it. You show them.' But could I?

On the last Friday in May, just before the Spring Bank Holiday week-end, I received a visit from a Trading Standards Officer, calling on behalf of MAFF. He had brought with him what was called a 'D Notice', which he said had to be displayed on my gate. The notice read in bold capital letters: 'NO ENTRY FOOT AND MOUTH DISEASE'

He told me that this also meant that I could not move any animals on or off my land, as if I did not already know this. I told him this notice was out of date, since it should have been served two months ago, following the outbreak at Warwick Holme Farm. He apologised and told me that Trading Standards were the last people to get to know anything that MAFF were up to. I waited until he had gone and removed the sign.

It was a mystery to me why now I was being served with this notice. More than two months had passed since the outbreak at Warwick Holme Farm that had brought me within a three kilometre zone. Some six weeks had passed since my appeal and solicitor's letter to MAFF and two weeks since their letter in response to that appeal. At no time had anyone from MAFF been on my premises. No tests had been carried out on my sheep. Yet here was a notice that I was apparently required to display proclaiming that my premises were infected.

It was just this sort of action in the run up to 7 June that fuelled the stories circulating in Cumbria that MAFF was biding its time until the Election was out of the way, before launching a mass cull of remaining livestock. It was rumoured that police leave had been cancelled and that more haulage contractors were being taken on to cope with the extra loads of dead animals.

On the Friday before the country went to the polls, Kath Smart reported in the *Cumberland News* how, although officially the number of confirmed cases in Cumbria totalled 718, in fact some 3,100 farms in Cumbria had had their animals slaughtered. The last agricultural census by MAFF for 1999 returned 6,344 farms in Cumbria. Even my arithmetic was good enough to work out that this meant almost half of the farms in the area had been wiped out.

But the statistic which I found staggering was that reportedly more than 1,800 Cumbrian farms had volunteered their sheep for slaughter under the 3 kilometre zone culling policy. For weeks one of the rumours going the rounds had been that the culling of sheep was deliberate because, it was said, there were far too many in the UK as a whole and the outbreak of foot and mouth was a golden opportunity to do something about reducing the numbers in one fell swoop. If that really were the case, then MAFF officials must have been rubbing their hands with glee at the readiness of farmers to surrender their sheep without a fight.

Less than a week later, it was Tony Blair who was rubbing his hands with glee as Labour was returned to power for a second term with another substantial parliamentary majority. By contrast, Agriculture Minister Nick Brown was left either wringing his hands or rubbing his backside, as he was unceremoniously moved from MAFF and demoted to the post of minister for work.

MAFF itself meanwhile was abolished as a separate department. Instead it was to be absorbed into a new 'super ministry' known as the Department of the Environment, Food and Rural Affairs, or DEFRA for short. All reference to agriculture or fisheries had gone with Mr Brown. The new minister in charge was Mrs Margaret Beckett. Would any of this, I wondered, make any difference to overall policy? Would any of this make any difference to me?

10

GIVING BLOOD

As it happened, there was an immediate difference made to policy and it did, potentially at least, make a difference to me. I received a letter from MAFF, dated 7 June 2001, the day of the General Election itself and possibly the last letter to be issued from Rosehill before the name change to DEFRA. The letter was from the 'Operations Manager - 3km cull' and was headed 'Cull of sheep, goats and pigs in North Cumbria'. No reference this time to 'camelids', I noticed.

By MAFF's standards it was quite a short letter. Perhaps they had known already that the department, or at least its stationery, was about to be culled and had wanted to rush the letters out quick while there was still time.

'In mid March,' the letter began, 'the Minister for Agriculture Fisheries & Food announced a policy to cull stock in the 3km zones around the dense cluster of Infected Premises in North Cumbria. A programme to remove live sheep to slaughter, and slaughter pigs on farm was put in place. Between 28 March and 21 May over 450,000 animals were processed through this scheme.'

'Processed through this scheme,' I sighed at the euphemism adopted. It was as if the author of the letter, having had the honesty to use the word 'slaughter' twice in the previous sentence, could not bring himself to repeat it again so soon, for fear of upsetting the reader.

'The programme was based on veterinary advice,' continued the letter. 'The Chief Veterinary Officer and MAFF's scientific advisors believed that the weight of infection in the area was so great that sheep and pigs in the area would have been exposed to infection.'

Then came the important bit as far as I was concerned. 'The disease situation in this area has improved. Veterinary advice is that it is no longer necessary to automatically slaughter animals in the 3km zones in North Cumbria. Instead groups of animals on every holding in each 3km zone will be subjected to blood tests. The result of the test will determine whether the animals have to be slaughtered.'

My first reaction to this was that, after slaughtering 450,000 animals, I should damn well hope that the disease situation would have improved, otherwise the whole exercise would have been even more futile than I had thought. I noted also that the writer had happily returned to 'slaughtering' instead of 'processing'.

But what I realised on re-reading this paragraph was that the writer was referring to 'animals' and 'groups of animals'. There was no singling out of rare breeds or other exceptions within the 3km zones. In other words, the distinction made previously by MAFF between my rare breed Ryelands, on the one hand, and my non-rare sheep, on the other, was no longer of importance. Everything would still depend on the result of blood tests. However, so long as these were successful, then Topsy, Fiver, the Blackies and all their lambs would be spared, along with Mr Universe and the Ryelands.

This was the best news I had had in a long time. If I had had the energy, I would have danced a little jig around the kitchen. Instead, I went outside and into the field. As ever, Topsy and Fiver, followed by their lambs, came galloping across to see me and were soon doing their best to rip my pockets so as to get at the biscuits, which they knew to be inside. As ever, the Blackies kept their distance.

I contacted Simon Leach at Burges Salmon. Again his view was that we should wait and see. The final paragraph of MAFF's letter had stated that those who had already made representations against the slaughter of their stock would be contacted shortly to explain how and when their stock would be dealt with. There seemed little point in making further representations at this stage.

Despite this latest development, I knew that I could not afford to drop my guard and that I must continue to be vigilant, both in checking my sheep daily and in carrying out my various biosecurity precautions. However, I decided that it would perhaps be safe to let the Ryelands out into the field, so long as I could find a way of continuing to separate them from the rest of my sheep. The answer, I was told, would be an electric fence so that I could cordon off one part of the field and know that sheep on either side of the fence would be deterred from crossing over to the other.

I contacted Jane Barribal at Farmtalking and she found a farmer in

West Cumbria who had an electric fence that I could have. Suzanne Greenhill, who had been arguing the case for hefted flocks, and her husband Peter, who headed the auction mart at Cockermouth, kindly offered to pay for the fence and Julian and Veronica Thurgood helpfully transported it across to Warwick Bridge. All I had to supply was a battery to activate the fence.

Once the fence had been set up, I was able to let the Ryelands out of the shed and onto the lush grass in the field. Actually, to call it lush is something of an overstatement. Not only was the grass much longer than it would have been, had the Ryelands been able to graze on it earlier in the year, but also there were all manner of nettles and weeds competing for attention. The Ryelands did not seem to mind. Until then, they had only been allowed outside the shed for brief periods and even then they had been confined to the small paddock next to my cottage. It was as if they had been prisoners locked up in a cell for 23 hours in the day and only allowed out for one hour's exercise around the prison compound. Except that most prisoners, I reflected, usually knew how long their sentence will last. As I stood watching the Ryelands on one side of the fence and Topsy and the rest on the other, I felt that at least all of my sheep had now been put on parole.

My last letter from MAFF was followed within a week by my first letter from DEFRA. It was headed in bold capital letters: 'LIFTING FOOT AND MOUTH RESTRICTIONS IN CUMBRIA'. Whereas the MAFF letter had barely run to a page and had been signed by the 'Operations Manager - 3km cull', the DEFRA letter was four pages long and had been signed by the disposals manager. Again, the subject of this letter was the change in policy towards the 3km zones, signified by the fact that these were now called 'Protection Zones' or PZ for short.

I thought that perhaps the name change to Protection Zone was a deliberate ploy, designed to lull one into a false sense of security. Indeed the whole tone of the letter was altogether softer than that of previous MAFF communications.

Having started by summarising the existing restrictions in place, it went on to outline a plan for lifting the 3km Protection Zones in Cumbria. DEFRA, the disposals manager said, would have to visit all farms in each PZ and carry out checks to ensure there were no signs of foot and mouth virus. The checks would include: blood sampling sheep and goats, veterinary inspection of all other animals and inspecting farm records, including animal movement records, use of medicines, mortality, abortion, feed and production records. If the visit revealed no signs of disease and any blood samples were negative, then arrangements would be made to remove the Protection Zone status as quickly as possible.

I read on, 'If inspection of animals or the blood tests show signs of disease then a further series of checks are necessary before the zone can be lifted.'

I am sorry I thought to myself, there must be some mistake. Let me read that last sentence again. 'If inspection of animals or the blood tests show signs of disease then a further series of checks are necessary before the zone can be lifted.'

Yes, I thought to myself, that is what I thought you said. But what happens to the animals? On this point, the disposals manager was silent, despite continuing his letter for another page and a half. I managed to get an answer to this question via Suzanne Greenhill who faxed me the comments of a DEFRA vet a few days later.

In short, the vet said that if the tests were negative, that meant what it said and the animals would remain alive. If the tests showed a single positive, there would be a further check. If a further sample showed positive, then that particular animal would be slaughtered but not the whole flock. Only if the further check revealed two or more positives would the whole flock be slaughtered. I wondered why the disposals manager could not have spelled that out in his letter.

Still, no matter, the fact was that events appeared to be moving in my favour. By digging in my heels and lodging an appeal against the original 3km policy announced in March, I had managed to hold out long enough for that policy first to be relaxed, at the end of April with the acceptance of an exception for rare breeds, and now, in early June, to be abandoned altogether in favour of blood tests on a case by case basis.

The disposals manager's letter concluded that there were over 700 infected premises in Cumbria and more than 3,000 premises within the Cumbrian Protection Zones. The work to tackle these might take three to four months 'or longer to complete in total'. I realised I could face a long wait before my turn came for blood testing.

In the meantime, there were worrying signs that foot and mouth was still far from finished in Cumbria. First, there was a sudden spate of cases south of Penrith. Next, came news that Trotters World of Animals at Bassenthwaite had lost all their animals in a cull, including sheep, pigs, goats, cattle, deer and llamas. Finally, one of the county's most important dairy farmers at Carleton, on the outskirts of Carlisle, was reported as having been hit by the disease. Any relief which I had felt at the change in policy announced by DEFRA was offset by anxiety at the continuing outbreaks. Clearly I could not afford to take any chances with letting up on my biosecurity measures. But would these be enough to see me through?

One bright spot in the midst of all this was to receive a letter inviting me to attend a meeting in Cockermouth at the end of September. The venue was to be Mitchell's Auction Mart, of which Peter Greenhill was chairman, and the principal visitor was to be none other than His Royal Highness, the Prince of Wales. That was something to look forward to, I thought, as I wondered what I should wear and what Chloe and Holly would think of my practice curtsies in the kitchen. Surely by then, I would have had my sheep blood tested and know the results?

July came and with it a letter from DEFRA asking about arrangements to come and carry out the blood tests. I wrote back to say that I was only prepared to proceed on the basis that my own vet carried out the tests. By now, there was enough anecdotal evidence about the casual approach of DEFRA's own officials to bio-security measures for me to be determined not to expose myself to the risk of having one of them on my premises. I did not want to be in the position of having a DEFRA vet come one day and be telephoned the next to be told that unfortunately the vet who had come out to see me was 'not clean' and therefore my animals would have to be treated as 'dangerous contacts' and summarily shot.

DEFRA replied that it would have to be one of their vets. I responded again that it would have to be my vet who came and that, unless he was allowed to do the testing, I would refuse to have them done at all, since I knew my sheep were in good health and wanted them to remain so. For good measure, I contacted the press again and told them of my fears of having a 'dirty' vet from DEFRA undertake the tests.

DEFRA conceded. My vet, Jonathan, telephoned me to ask when he could come and test my sheep. D-day, or perhaps that should be T-day, was fixed for Wednesday 25 July.

The evening before, my friend Norman brought his collie and together they rounded up the Blackies into one corner of the field, which was penned off, so that they could not stray. Otherwise it would not have mattered whether the vet was Jonathan or from DEFRA, because no one would have been able to catch a Blackie to carry out the test. The Ryelands of course all came into the shed without any bother and without any need of prompting from Norman's collie.

The following day I had organised it so that Tim, the husband of one of my demonstration friends, Amanda, and one of his employees came to help hold the sheep, so that all Jonathan had to concentrate on was taking the blood. Jonathan had told me that the tests would be taken as one job lot but I said that this was completely unacceptable. I wanted to have all of the sheep numbered, so that if any test came back positive, it would be possible to single out immediately which of the sheep was the source and a further test could be carried out on that particular animal. If one were screening sixty women for breast cancer, surely each test would have a name allocated to it? Why, I argued, should it be any different with testing sixty sheep?

In the event, with the help of the two lads pressed into service, Jonathan was able to take all the blood tests required without too much difficulty. Even the Blackies were reasonably docile, although as soon as the testing was completed and their pen removed they set off in a mad dash for the far corner of the field. It was now a case of simply crossing one's fingers and waiting for the results, which I was told were unlikely to come back for some weeks. There was nothing further that I could do.

Two days after the blood testing, I travelled down to a meeting at Penrith Rugby Club to mark the launch of the 'Heart of Cumbria' campaign. Heart of Cumbria was modelled on Heart of Devon, a group set up by the TV personality, Noel Edmonds, in response to the outbreak of foot and mouth in the south west. One of the founders of Heart of Cumbria was my fellow attendee of numerous demonstrations, the climbing and mountaineering instructor with the megaphone voice, Nick Green. Nick had helped organise and chaired the meeting.

The speakers included Penrith and Borders MP, David Maclean, who had been a source of much support to me and countless other farmers and smallholders, Dr Richard North, who I had first heard speak weeks earlier on the subject of vaccination at the Farmers for Action meeting and a retired hospital virologist, Ruth Watkins, who I learnt had posted a paper advocating vaccination on the internet back in March.

There were more than three hundred in the audience, including many farmers from both Cumbria and North Yorkshire. Also present was NFU representative and cattle farmer, Les Armstrong, who had lost his herd at an early stage in the outbreak. Despite this experience, Les was not apparently persuaded by the arguments in favour of vaccination. Judging from the attitude of those present, he was very much in the minority. When he asked the audience if they wanted vaccination, several shouted back that they did and a show of hands confirmed that the majority agreed.

Overall the meeting was excellent and gave my morale a greatly need-ed boost. It was particularly interesting to talk to some of the farmers from North Yorkshire, bearing in mind my own telephone contacts with Pat Walker and other smallholders from that area. They were all incensed at the way things had been handled. On returning home, I was suffi-ciently fired up to dash off a strongly worded letter to the Prime Minister on the subject of vaccination.

A few days later, a letter arrived from 10 Downing Street.

'Dear Mrs Linaker,

'The Prime Minister has asked me to thank you for your recent letter and to tell you that the views you expressed have been carefully noted.

'Yours sincerely'

I noted that the letter was headed 'From the Direct Communications Unit'. Presumably the government's spin doctors worked for the Indirect Communications Unit.

Ever since the General Election in June, there had been growing pres-sure for a public inquiry into the handling of the foot and mouth out-break. In July, Channel 4's *Dispatches* had broadcast a searching review of the government's handling of the crisis in its initial stages. Both Agriculture Minister Nick Brown and MAFF Chief Vet Jim Scudamore had been strongly criticised for their approach and the government's chief scientific adviser Professor David King and the team of epidemiol-ogists at Imperial College, London, led by Professor Roy Anderson, had been presented as the heroes of the crisis coming to the rescue of a floun-dering MAFF.

The latter's computer model had apparently shown that delays in the first three weeks of the crisis over first slaughter and then disposal had been instrumental in dramatically increasing the number of cases. As a result, Professor Anderson's team had advocated a new strategy to combat the spread of foot and mouth. First, all infected animals must be killed within 24 hours. Secondly, all animals on farms within the three-kilometre zone surrounding an outbreak of foot and mouth must be killed within 48 hours. In short, it was Anderson's team that had come up with the 'contiguous cull' strategy and Professor King who had embraced this as the solution, at the same time as he had taken over control of the crisis from MAFF before the end of March.

The possibility of vaccination as an alternative or complementary approach to slaughter was touched on in the documentary but it was apparent that neither Professor Anderson's team nor the NFU leadership were going to recommend this and the moment passed. I hoped that any subsequent inquiry would look at the question of vaccination more searchingly.

Meanwhile I was on tenterhooks waiting for the results of the blood tests. As each day passed, I was worrying more and more. What if the samples got lost? What if they got mixed up? Could they have been contaminated en route to or subsequently during examination? On Monday 6 August, I received a telephone call from Jonathan, my vet.

'Moira,' he said, 'I am delighted to be able to tell you that all of the blood test results have come back negative. All of your sheep are in the clear.'

I was ecstatic but, even then, I do not think I fully believed that my sheep had been reprieved until the next day when I received written confirmation from DEFRA. Negative. Negative. Negative.

All of a sudden this seemed to be the most beautiful word in the English language. I felt exhausted and elated at one and the same time. After all these weeks, after all these months, my sheep - all of my sheep - were safe.

I had won my battle.

11

THE ROTTWEILER

While I might have won my own battle, I still could not be sure that I would win the war. In Cumbria as a whole, the situation did not seem to be getting any better during August. What had become known as 'the Penrith Spur' had been increased in size by DEFRA to prevent the spread of foot and mouth to other areas of the county and beyond. It was reported that a five million pound fund to help Cumbria's tourist related businesses recover from losses caused by foot and mouth had run out of cash because demand from affected firms had been so high. And as the end of the month drew near, there came worrying news from across the border in Northumberland of fresh outbreaks, after that county had enjoyed - if that is the right word to use - a disease free interlude of three months.

As the *Cumberland News* observed on 31 August, 'The most worrying aspect is that, after all the slaughter, restrictions and bio-security measures, the spread of foot and mouth remains largely unpredictable and unchecked. It demands concerted and urgent action but, six months on, the experts still cannot agree how to go about it.'

By then, the government had announced the setting up of not one but three inquiries. These were to consider separately: the government's administrative handling of the crisis, how animal diseases should be handled in future and the future of farming itself. There was to be no one comprehensive inquiry into foot and mouth. Nor were any of the separate inquiry hearings to be held in public.

For me personally, there was further good news when I received a letter in early September from DEFRA to say that all of the blood samples and veterinary inspections on animals within my particular Protection Zone had proved negative. DEFRA's letter was accompanied by a Form E notice, which cancelled the Form D notice that I had been issued with by the trading standards officer back in May. However, the letter itself stressed that, because Cumbria remained within the Infected Area Restrictions, I would not be able to move animals without a licence from

DEFRA and that I should continue with the same stringent bio-security measures previously enforced under the Form D notice.

(Amazingly, or perhaps not so amazingly in the case of DEFRA, three weeks later I was to receive another Form E notice dated 28 September, which was identical in every respect to the first one except for the name of the official who had signed it. Ironically the name of this second official was Anderson. These Andersons get everywhere I thought. First there was Professor Anderson and his computer modelling. Next there was Dr Iain Anderson who had been appointed to head the inquiry into the government's administrative handling of the outbreak. Now here was A S Anderson, an inspector from the Animal Health Office at Rosehill, dishing out Form E notices.)

I did not need DEFRA to remind me that I should not drop my guard. So far, there had been barely a day in September when there had not been at least one further confirmed case of foot and mouth in Cumbria. Lord Haskins, who had been appointed chairman of the Cumbrian foot and mouth task force by the government, was reported in the *News & Star* to have said that preventative vaccination of livestock would have to be considered if outbreaks continued.

'If present arrangements are not seen to be working we will have to consider a radical change of attitude towards the issue. I started like everybody else saying slaughter was the best policy. Many of us have changed our minds.'

Not everybody of course had started by saying that slaughter was the best policy. Some experts had advocated vaccination from the outset and three of these: Professor Fred Brown, Dr Simon Barteling and Dr Paul Sutmoller were invited by Heart of Cumbria to address a meeting in Penrith. I went along to join an audience of hundreds, including many farmers and vets, at the Hired Lad at Penrith Farmers & Kidd's auction mart.

I was aware that some other advocates of vaccination had had doubts cast over their credentials but there could be no disputing the qualifications and experience of the three speakers. Professor Brown, a Fellow of the Royal Society, had worked with foot and mouth since 1955 and was visiting scientist at the United States Department of Agriculture's Animal Disease Centre. Dr Barteling was an international consultant on foot and mouth and formerly head of the European Union Community Co-ordinating Institute for Foot and Mouth Disease. Dr Sutmoller was a vet who had worked for more than 35 years as a virologist and epidemiologist on the prevention, control and eradication of foot and mouth in Latin America and the Caribbean.

Professor Brown told the audience that in March MAFF had been asked if the foot and mouth outbreak could be used to validate a test, which was able to detect all 70 types of foot and mouth in two hours. MAFF had responded that it was currently overwhelmed with what it had to do but that 'maybe later' this could be tried. Dr Barteling warned that the virus in Cumbria was a 'guerrilla' strain, which often went underground, and that re-stocking in an unvaccinated situation was highly risky. Dr Sutmoller pointed out that people in the United Kingdom had been eating meat from vaccinated cattle imported from South America for 30 years.

This last point had always struck me as making a mockery of the arguments over the United Kingdom losing its 'disease free' status if it embarked on a programme of vaccination. If you went into any supermarket and looked at the meat counter you would see meat labelled as having been 'packed to British Farm Standards'. But if you read the small print you would see its source described as, for example, 'Brazil vaccinated animals.' Yet we were being told constantly by leaders of the NFU and by government ministers that British consumers would not stand for vaccinated meat.

Not that Margaret Beckett, the minister in charge of DEFRA, who had replaced Nick Brown at the time of the General Election in June, appeared to have any interest in what was happening in Cumbria. Carlisle City Council had sent her a letter shortly after her appointment asking her to make a fact-finding visit to the area. Three months had passed since the invitation and, according to the council leader quoted in the *News & Star*, DEFRA had sent nothing more substantial than 'a little white postcard saying the request has been noted.' It was reported that Mrs Beckett intended to visit Cumbria 'when time allows.' This hardly demonstrated an appreciation that the situation in the county was still serious.

24 September was the day when I had to go and meet Prince Charles. I arranged to have my sheep guarded and set off on the 40 minute drive to Cockermouth. The weather could not have been worse. There was torrential rain all the way so that the 40 minute drive turned into more

like an hour, especially as, once out of Carlisle, I did not know the way and kept getting lost. I have never had much sense of direction and I was hugely relieved when I eventually arrived in Cockermouth itself, parked the car and managed to find the auction mart.

The meeting was actually held at Mitchell's Fine Art Auction Rooms and inside there must have been about 60 farmers and their wives, all of whom had lost their stock. In most cases this had not been because their animals had gone down with foot and mouth but because they had been caught by the three kilometre cull. While I chatted to various couples, I felt somewhat embarrassed to be in their company, as the only one who still had her sheep.

Also present were all the local mayors and other dignitaries. Over the years, I have been to a few functions but I had never before seen so many chains of office in one place.

His Royal Highness arrived, followed by Elizabeth Buchanan, his assistant private secretary, who by now I knew quite well as a result of our many telephone conversations. The Prince's bodyguard followed Elizabeth. The Prince sat down at one of the tables amongst us and asked us to describe our personal experiences and how foot and mouth had affected us. At first, the farmers were a little shy but the Prince soon put every one at their ease and gradually they took turns to give their own personal stories. He was very understanding and I was impressed at just how aware he was of the situation in Cumbria.

As we approached the end of the meeting, I noticed Elizabeth Buchanan beckoning the bodyguard who was standing against the wall. She whispered something in his ear and with that he began walking around the outside of the ring and stopped behind me. I felt my face flush and go as red as the jacket that I was wearing.

'Are you Mrs Linaker?' asked the bodyguard.

All heads turned towards me to see what was going on.

'Yes,' I replied, a little unsteadily. I could hardly deny my identity.

'Would you follow me please,' said the bodyguard.

How I managed to stand up and follow him I just do not know. I was conscious that the audience was following my every move and my legs felt like lead weights. Eventually the bodyguard stopped beside Elizabeth, who immediately stood up and kissed me on the cheek. She told me His Royal Highness wished to have a private word with me and would I go and stand beside the door by which the Prince was soon to leave.

I had to walk across the ring to the door and it seemed to move farther and farther away as I did so. At last I made it and shortly afterwards the Prince wished every one all the best for the future and began walking towards me, with Elizabeth leading the way. When she was quite close, she turned to the Prince to introduce me. Prince Charles smiled and said there was no need to introduce me, as he knew exactly who this was.

I was so flustered that I forgot to curtsy, even though I had been practising for days in the kitchen, much to the confusion of my two dogs, who could not understand what I was doing. We spoke for some five minutes and, although I cannot repeat our conversation, I can say how sympathetic and kind he was.

I had brought with me the registration certificate for Harry. For his formal registered name, I had chosen D'Artganan, from *The Three Musketeers*, which I had discovered meant 'defender of the crown'. Harry had been registered in the name of His Royal Highness but we agreed that some time would have to elapse before he could be transferred physically to what would be his new home at Highgrove.

On my return home later that evening, my eldest son, Peter, who lives in Oxford, telephoned me and asked if I wanted a computer. He was upgrading to another one and, if I would like to have his old one, he would come up to Warwick Bridge and set it up for me. I had never operated a computer in my life but, after thinking about it for a day or two, I decided that I would give it a go.

And so Peter arrived with the computer and set it up in my spare bedroom and all of a sudden I was on line. Peter showed me the basics and then he had to return to Oxford. After he had gone, I kept looking at the thing all evening. I did not have the courage to switch it on. Eventually I lost my bottle completely and even switched it off at the wall. I was terrified of it. Even the qwerty keyboard was a complete mystery to me, as I had never been trained to use a typewriter or word processor.

I realised that I would have to get some tuition and I saw advertised at the local school a six-week course called 'Computers for Beginners'. I went along and signed up. After the first two hour lesson I had enough confidence to actually go onto the internet and after the second week I was able to manage an e-mail. I was determined to master my computer and by the end of the six weeks I felt quite confident.

Having access to the internet and e-mail really did open up a whole new world to me. In retrospect I wished that I had done this before the outbreak of foot and mouth, as I would have had immediate access to so much information from websites, such as Peter Kindersley's sheep-drove.com, Mary Critchley's warmwell.com and Alan and Rosie Beat's smallholders.org, rather than having to rely on getting hold of this second hand. Access to e-mail also made it easier to communicate quickly with the wide variety of friends that I had made during the foot and mouth crisis, including my American pen pals, Sandie in Seattle, Barbara in Wisconsin and Mary June in Ypsilanti, Michigan.

I even ended up with my own website, which was created for me free of charge by Julian Thurgood from Cockermouth. Julian had previously developed the Heart of Cumbria website so that I knew I was in good hands. Starting with a few pages of text about the Ryelands and some of my own photographs, he gradually extended the website to include links with press stories that had appeared on the BBC and other national websites and has continued to update the site ever since.

By the end of September 2001 cases of foot and mouth in Cumbria had at last become a trickle. In fact, although one did not know at the time, the last confirmed case was on 30 September. Because it was getting near to the tupping (or mating) season those farmers that still had sheep were looking to bring in rams to put with their ewes so as to have early lambs. DEFRA agreed that sheep could be sold but only under very strict conditions, which included the blood testing of all the sheep by one of their vets. The farmer or smallholder also had to complete a 25 page form as a prerequisite to securing a movement licence and, once an animal had been brought on to your land, you were then on a 14 day standstill, which meant that nothing could be moved on or off your farm or holding during that time.

In October I was approached by someone who had lost his stock in a cull and who wanted to restart by breeding some Ryelands. He asked if I had a ram and ewe for sale and I said yes. I thought that by now it would be safe to let a DEFRA vet come out and blood test the sheep to be sold, so I made arrangements for a visit.

The day came and a car pulled on to my drive and a very tall man and a young woman got out. I went out and ushered both dogs into the cottage so that they were not in the way, while the man and woman first stood in the tray of disinfectant at the end of my drive and then put on their waterproofs. I had put the ram and the ewe that I was going to sell in the shed, while leaving the rest of the Ryelands out in the field. I noticed that neither the man nor the woman was wearing a mask and I stopped them before they got to my gate.

'Where are your masks?' I asked them.

'We haven't brought any,' replied the man.

'Well, you're not going into that shed and near my sheep unless you've each got a mask,' I said, 'Wait there and I'll get you some.'

I went back into the cottage to find each of them a mask. All through the months of foot and mouth I had never gone into the shed in which I had housed the Ryelands without wearing a mask and rubber gloves. Then, when I had come out of the shed I had disposed of both gloves and mask.

I gave them the masks and said to the vet, 'You haven't been on a dirty farm have you?'

'No,' he said. He had come up from the Brecon Beacons in South Wales. I was concerned at this because FMD had been raging in the Beacons but he assured me that he had not been on any infected farms so I let him and his assistant proceed.

They put on their masks and rubber gloves, which I had to give them also, and I led them into the shed. The DEFRA vet decided he would start with the ewe and produced a yellow plastic sealed square bottle and a hypodermic. Usually, in my experience, a vet shaves off an area of wool before attempting to get at the vein of a sheep but I noticed that this vet did not do this. But then, I thought, some of these vets are very clever and can manage to take blood without having to shave first. Only this one was not. He started stabbing the ewe through her thick wool, as if she were a pincushion, and I soon realised that he did not know what he was doing. Eventually he hit a vein all right. He hit an artery. Blood was pouring out everywhere from the ewe and I could feel my blood boiling.

He filled his plastic bottle - he could have filled a bucket - and came out of the pen holding the ewe. He started to move to the other pen where the ram was standing.

'Hey!' I shouted, 'hang on a minute. What are you going to do about the state of this ewe with all this blood?'

'Have you got a piece of cotton wool?' he replied.

'Cotton wool?' I said, 'You've got to be joking.'

He stood and looked at me.

'Right,' I said, 'That's it. Don't touch that ram. Leave him alone. I want you off my premises now. I'm going to have to call my vet to look at this ewe. This is the first time I've had DEFRA on my property and, so far as I'm concerned, it will be the last.'

As he came away from the ram, he picked up the bottle containing the blood taken from the ewe.

'What are you doing with that?' I asked.

'Well, it's got to go back to DEFRA.'

'Oh no it hasn't,' I said, 'That's from my sheep. You're on my premises, that's my blood and it stays here.'

'But I've got to test the whole flock.'

'You must be joking if you think I'm going to let you anywhere near the rest of my sheep after what you've done to that ewe. You haven't a clue what you're doing.' By this time I was really wound up.

'Look,' I continued, with a conviction belying the fact that I was a woman standing at five feet nothing confronting a man well over six feet in height towering over me, 'You either give me that blood voluntarily or I shall take it by force.' He looked at me quizzically.

I pulled my trump card. 'If you're not off my land in two minutes, I shall get my doberman out of the house and set it loose on you and, as for what's left of you after that, I shall get my gun and shoot you. The time starts now. So you had better give me that blood.'

That did it. He shakily gave me the bottle and hared off towards the gate with the assistant following close behind. They shut the gate and jumped in the car, without pausing to step again in the tray of disinfectant, and drove off at speed as if they were Starsky and Hutch or Cagney and Lacey (or perhaps that should be Starsky and Lacey).

I went into the cottage and got some ice out of the freezer. I returned to the shed and put an ice pack round the ewe's neck. I then rang Jonathan, my vet, and asked him to come out and look at the ewe, because she was shaking and clearly traumatised. I then rang DEFRA and told the official to whom I spoke that I wanted to make a formal complaint about their vet's conduct. I was told that I could not do this. I responded that there was no way that I was allowing either him or another vet from DEFRA back on to my property. The official then asked what I was going to do if I still wanted to sell the ram and ewe. I told him that I would have my own vet carry out the blood tests. 'Oh!' was all he could say.

Jonathan arrived a few minutes later at the cottage.

'Moira,' he said, 'what on earth's happened. I've had DEFRA on the phone telling me that a crazy woman from Warwick Bridge has threatened to shoot one of their vets. I knew it was you because no one else at Warwick Bridge has any sheep.'

'Yes,' I said, 'it was me.'

'Have you got a gun?' asked Jonathan.

'No, of course not,' I replied, 'But he wasn't to know that.'

Jonathan checked over the ewe. The ice pack had stopped the bleeding and the ewe was starting to calm down. He said that if I could make arrangements for someone to help hold the sheep, he would come and blood test the flock next day so that I could apply for a licence.

The following day he came back and blood tested the whole flock without any problems, apart from a little difficulty with Mr Universe who did not take kindly to this indignity. A fortnight later the test results came back negative and the ram and ewe were on their way.

I do not know for certain but I believe it may have been as a result of this episode that I acquired a nickname with the staff at the local office of DEFRA. Although I only found out much later, I was now known as 'The Rottweiler'

12

Animal Health?

While concerns might have been diminishing over foot and mouth, sheep breeders, and particularly those with rare breeds, were becoming exercised about another development specifically aimed at them, which was the National Scrapie Plan. The first communication I received on this was from DEFRA. However its National Scrapie Plan Administration Centre in Worcester was obviously under the impression that my smallholding was in Wales because the letter was written entirely in Welsh, apart from the name of the official who had signed it.

'Yn gywir' to you too, Mr Penny, I thought. Obviously the global positioning systems inherited from MAFF were malfunctioning.

Fortunately, DEFRA's letter was soon followed by a series of letters and information sheets from the Rare Breeds Survival Trust. One of these told me the following:

'Scrapie is a disease of sheep. There has never been a recorded case in humans. To suffer from scrapie a sheep must be both genetically susceptible and exposed to the infective agent (a prion). There is a gene called PrP in sheep, which interacts with the scrapie prion. This gene has five forms, three of which give degrees of resistance to scrapie, one of which is very susceptible to scrapie and another of which increases the possibility of infection by BSE/v-CJD.

'The government wishes to remove the scrapie and BSE/v-CJD susceptible varieties from the commercial sheep population to minimise the risk of occurrence of BSE in sheep.

'Some rare breeds of sheep are likely to either lack or contain at very low frequencies the resistant forms of the gene. These breeds are at risk from the legislation.'

If one were to believe in conspiracy theories, it might appear that the government had embarked on the National Scrapie Plan as a means of finishing off those sheep left over after the decimation of foot and mouth. In effect, the consequences of the plan for commercial breeds were summed up by the Rare Breeds Survival Trust as 'humane slaughter or castration of all highly susceptible sheep.' Clearly the RBST wished to protect rare breeds from such a fate.

By now I had had to learn a new acronym TSE, which stood for 'Transmissible Spongiform Encephalopathies'. Although sounding as if they were something out of Mary Poppins, these were anything but supercalifragilisticexpialidocious. TSEs are degenerative diseases of the central nervous system resulting in the brain eventually ceasing to function. Scrapie was apparently the first form of SE to be recognised and had been around for more than two hundred years. BSE, the bovine form, had been found in cattle only in 1985.

It was speculated that scrapie could be linked in some way to BSE, which in turn had been blamed as the cause of some outbreaks of vCJD among humans. BSE had never been found in sheep but the government and Food Standards Agency had decided that they were not taking any risks.

I was not taking any either. I decided that there was no way I was going to allow DEFRA to carry out scrapie tests on my Ryelands, after the recent harrowing experience of one of their vets. I told both DEFRA and the RBST that I would have my two Ryeland rams, Mr Universe and Titan, tested privately at my own expense. And so it was time for yet another visit from my vet, Jonathan, and at a cost of £52 each the samples were sent away to the Central Diagnostic Laboratory of Scottish Agricultural College's Veterinary Science Division at Penicuick, just outside Edinburgh. I was told the results should be back in about a month's time, which would mean the end of November.

Not long after the scrapie tests, yet another potential threat appeared on the scene. At the end of October, the government introduced an Animal Health Bill in the House of Commons. It was so called because it proposed a series of amendments to the 1981 Animal Health Act. In all other respects however, it was a complete misnomer. As MP David Maclean, who led four votes against the bill, said, 'This is not an animal health bill but an animal extermination bill.'

The new bill greatly increased DEFRA's powers of slaughter. Under existing legislation only animals which were infected or suspected of being infected with foot and mouth (or other disease), or which had been in contact with infected animals or exposed to the disease could be slaughtered. By contrast, the bill allowed for any animal, including horses, dogs and pets, to be slaughtered wherever this was deemed necessary for disease control reasons. It would allow for the widespread and indiscriminate culling of animals, including animals that had been vaccinated against foot and mouth and other diseases. The bill also gave DEFRA extensive new powers of entry to farmers' property and of sanctions and penalties against farmers, while redress against DEFRA failure was severely limited.

I was incensed. What did the government think it was doing? The foot and mouth crisis had only just come to an end and there were three enquiries still in progress. Yet here was the government apparently charging ahead with a range of new measures. Could they and should they not have waited for the results and recommendations of the enquiries? I felt as helpless and exasperated as Basil Fawlty in an episode of *Fawlty Towers*. 'What is the point?' I shouted to myself, 'I mean, what is the bloody point?'

Susan Bull was equally incensed, when I discussed the bill with her. 'This country is becoming more and more like a police state,' she thundered. 'We didn't - at least my father didn't - fight Hitler all those years ago just to end up with a bunch of jackboots at Westminster and Whitehall. We must do something, Moira.'

So we agreed, as a starting point, to get up a petition against the bill. Then, when we had collected sufficient signatures, at the suggestion of the Mayor, Doreen Parsons, I wrote to Carlisle City Council and asked if I could attend a council meeting to present this. I received a reply agreeing to my request but adding that I would only be allowed five minutes to speak. The time and date would be notified in due course.

At the end of the third week in November, I received the scrapie genotyping results from the SAC Central Diagnostic Laboratory. Both Mr Universe and Titan had been genotyped as 'ARR/ARR', which was the best possible result and meant that they were highly resistant to scrapie. The results were displayed on a certificate and I asked Doreen if she would like to come and present this to me so that we could get some press publicity for scrapie testing. She agreed and invited Jonathan along as well.

The three of us gathered together early in December for the presentation and were photographed with Doreen and Jonathan holding the certificate and me holding Mr Universe, resplendent in his blue overcoat. The main headline to the accompanying article was, 'Rare flock fights off scrapie test threat.' The second and smaller headline said, 'Moira snubs new DEFRA challenge.'

In the meantime, with my newly gained access to the internet and e-mail, I was busily gathering as much information as I could on the Animal Health Bill and corresponding with a number of MPs and peers who shared my views. In the event, I was disappointed that the bill was passed in the House of Commons without amendment on 13 December but heartened by the knowledge that it would be given a rough ride in the House of Lords.

As Christmas drew near, I thought I would send Christmas cards to every one who had been kind enough to send me letters and cards of encouragement over the past year. With help from a friend, I managed to print my own cards showing a picture of my sheep so that I could assure all of these well wishers that, after all the trauma of the year, the flock was still going strong.

Indeed the flock was about to be strengthened just in time for Christmas. On 23 December one of my ewes unexpectedly gave birth to twins and the Christmas Eve editions of various newspapers carried a picture of me holding them both and describing them as a symbol of hope for the New Year. As one was a ram and the other a ewe, I named them Peter and Suzanne after the Greenhills, in recognition of their tireless support.

At the beginning of January 2002 I received a letter from the city solicitor at Carlisle council informing me that my petition would be heard at 6.45pm on 15 January in the council chamber at the Civic Centre. I was invited to address the council, reminded that I should speak for not more than five minutes and told that members of the council would be circulated with a copy of the Animal Health Bill in advance.

Coincidentally, the day before I was due to appear before the council, the Animal Health Bill had its second reading in the House of Lords. Introducing this for the government, DEFRA minister Lord Whitty said that the government would be acting irresponsibly if, being aware of 'a major defect in the powers that are available to them,' they did not introduce corrective legislation.

This appeared tantamount to an admission that the government's action during the 2001 cull had not been within the law as it stood, a point which was taken up by more than one member of the Lords in the subsequent debate.

Lady Mallalieu (herself a distinguished barrister and furthermore a Labour peeress) commented that, 'the bill has been introduced in a way that goes far beyond what the Minister suggested were the necessary reasons. It gives virtually unlimited powers, providing DEFRA officials with, in effect, carte blanche to order slaughter without any requirement that they publicly justify, explain, give reasons, provide a fair hearing or, in some circumstances, compensate properly those whose animals are destroyed.'

The Countess of Mar (with whom I had corresponded) observed that the foot and mouth research station at Pirbright had been set up as long ago as 1924 as a result of criticism of the Ministry of Agriculture's primitive slaughter policy. 'Nothing much seems to have changed in the intervening period,' she added. 'From the beginning of the recent outbreak it was clear that no one had learnt any lessons from the past when they embarked on the mass slaughter of so many animals, the majority of which it seems, were healthy. It was not the largest outbreak in the world, but it was the one in which the most animals were killed.'

The numbers of animals killed were indeed staggering. At the end of September 2001, DEFRA's website showed the total number of premises on which animals had been or were due to be slaughtered at 9,503. The total number of animals slaughtered or identified for slaughter was 3,905,000 but in addition a further 1,751,786 animals had been slaughtered under the welfare disposal scheme, making an official grand total of 5,656,786.

However, as *Farmers' Weekly* had pointed out, these figures did not include calves, lambs and piglets, which were estimated at another 2,000,000. Therefore, the total number of animals killed was reckoned to be in the region of 7.7 million. To put that another way, the foot and mouth cull of 2001 had accounted for one out of every eight farm animals in Britain. In the face of this, the government's apparently best response was to come up with a bill that would enable a future cull to be even easier and more draconian than the one that had just been completed.

Was it any wonder that, when I read the following sent me by Peter

Greenhill, I had to read it twice to be sure that it was meant as a joke:

With immediate effect the NHS will be run by DEFRA with the following main targets:

❏ *All patients on waiting lists for more than 30 months will be culled.*

❏ *All family members of a sick person will be treated as dangerous contacts and culled.*

❏ *Neighbours within a 10km radius of a sick person will be treated as contagious contacts and culled.*

❏ *Any fit person will undergo a blood test. The discovery of antibodies will result in them being culled.*

❏ *Corpses will be either buried or burned as is the current custom.*

❏ *Licences must be obtained by people wishing to re-stock their families.*

The day came for my visit to Carlisle City Council with the petition. Susan Bull came with me to give moral support and, once I was inside, it was a help seeing Doreen sitting among the councillors in the chamber. I had worked hard on my address and practised and practised to make sure that I would not go beyond my allotted five minutes. I did not want to have the embarrassment of being stopped in mid-flow with an, 'I am sorry, Mrs Linaker, but that is all we have time for!'

'Madam Mayor and members of the council,' I began, 'many thousands of farmers, myself included, endured what can only be described as sheer hell for most of last year due to foot and mouth.

'Three weeks into disease free status and for the few fortunate enough to still have their stock a time for celebration? Unfortunately, not. Why?

'A new Animal Health Bill whose purpose appears to be to allow animals to be killed more easily and more quickly.

'Madam Mayor, I would like to draw your attention to just a few of the provisions in this so called Animal Health Bill. Provisions that raise matters of fundamental concern should this bill become law.

'Part 1 of the bill concerns slaughter. This extends the range of animals and categories of animals including family pets, whether it be your cat, dog or even your budgerigar.

'A right of appeal? Yes, there is. But since animals are to be shot on suspicion that would be pointless once they were dead.

'Paragraph 29 provides a power of entry for inspectors or police officers onto private property using reasonable force and, if considered necessary, a power to seize and retain records.

'Paragraph 35 provides a power of entry for the purpose of ascertaining whether any power to cause animals to be slaughtered should be exercised, and continues with Part 3 - Enforcement making further provision for powers of entry.

'Paragraph 40, Clause 9, provides a new power for inspectors to inspect vehicles to check compliance with disease free control measures and the inspector will be accompanied by a uniformed police officer.

'Paragraph 41, Clause 10, makes it clear that anyone who is considered to be obstructing an inspector or police officer will be arrested.

'Madam Mayor, in the last year some eight million farm animals were culled as part of the strategy to prevent the spread of foot and mouth. Yet all of the evidence that has since come to light shows that only a fraction of those animals were infected with foot and mouth or incubating the disease.

'In other words, most of the animals were needlessly slaughtered and much of the human and animal suffering could have been avoided. And yet, if this bill is enacted, the government will have even greater powers to override the civil liberties of farmers and to embark on a further round of animal destruction.

'Madam Mayor, it has become apparent that the approach used last year to combat foot and mouth in Cumbria and elsewhere in the United Kingdom was totally at odds with that favoured by the rest of the European Union and in other parts of the world.

'I submit that the present Animal Health Bill can only widen this gap. Instead of rushing into ill considered and potentially damaging legislation, the government should await the outcome of the various enquiries currently in progress and should consult more widely as to how foot and mouth and other farm animal diseases should be countered more effectively and more humanely.

'Madam Mayor and members of the city council, I ask you to accept this petition.'

There was utter silence in the council chamber when I had finished. I am quite sure that I could have continued for another five, ten or fifteen minutes and that no one would have stopped me. I had the total backing of everyone present, with the exception of one member, the Labour Group Leader, who tried to oppose my petition by stating that the Animal Health Bill would simply allow the government to act more quickly in the event of future outbreaks. She was shouted down and never did finish what she wanted to say.

It was proposed that my petition should be forwarded to Cumbria County Council and a few days letter I received a letter from the city solicitor confirming that this had been done and congratulating me on my presentation. My objections to the bill also received wide coverage in the local press (helped by another picture of the Christmas lambs, Peter and Suzanne). Soon afterwards it was announced that Cumbria would hold its own independent inquiry into foot and mouth, following the example of Devon, which had already decided to do this.

Back at home I was trying to get back to normal in preparation for lambing. One of the problems resulting from having had to keep the Ryelands indoors for so long during foot and mouth was that they had developed sore feet. As I could not manage the knack of turning them over to treat these, I needed to find someone to help. Colin Randall, vicar of the church next to my smallholding, suggested Robert Crozier.

'What he doesn't know about sheep isn't worth knowing,' said Colin.

So Robert began to look after my Ryelands' feet and, in the course of doing so, has given me all sorts of other useful tips about sheep. All the sheep seemed to like him, which is unusual because, as a general rule, my sheep are suspicious of men, being more used to women.

I had never had so many ewes in lamb before, because I still had most of those born in 2001 and they were now going to have lambs of their own. Needless to say in the case of the Blackies, last year's grown lambs were just as wild as their mothers.

Predictably Topsy was the first to lamb. I sat talking to her in the early hours of the morning and when she began to lamb she did not need any assistance. The second lamb came within twenty minutes of the first and I was busy dressing their navels, when a third arrived. Good old Topsy, I thought, three lambs yet again. What a mother.

I thought too soon. Topsy kept pushing the third lamb towards me and refused to lick it. I kept pushing the lamb back to her but, no, she had clearly decided that this year two lambs were quite enough and she could not be doing with feeding a third. I left it as long as possible but in the end there was nothing for it. I had to take the poor little thing myself and give it a bottle.

I kept it in a pen with another pet lamb and each morning Topsy would go and visit her lamb and then turn to look at me, as if to say, 'Well done. I knew you would look after it for me.' She continued these morning visits until the lamb was big enough to cope outside and happily accepted its company with her other two. But I was the mug who fed the lamb three times each day until it grew up.

Inevitably my thoughts returned to this time the year before and it was put to me that it would be good to do something in memory of all the animals that had died so needlessly during the foot and mouth crisis. I sought suggestions from friends and eventually decided on a tree planting ceremony. A weeping willow seemed an appropriate tree but deciding on an appropriate place to plant was more difficult. So far as I was concerned, Great Orton was out of the question. I could not bear to think of planting a tree in that place where so many animals had met such a horrible death before being buried.

I decided to write to Harrison & Hetherington, the local auctioneers at Rosehill. They had just finished building a new frontage and had plenty of grass and beds where a tree could be prominently displayed and I knew would be looked after. Furthermore their offices were right next to the Shepherds Inn, where all of the significant meetings of ministers and officials had taken place in the early stages of the crisis. I wrote to the chief executive with my proposal and he gave it his full support.

I then had to think of someone suitable to plant the tree and decided to approach Radio Cumbria's Anne Hopper, who I felt had been the voice of Cumbria during the dark days of foot and mouth with her daily broadcasts on the developing crisis. I wrote to Anne with a suggested date and to my delight she accepted.

And so on 26 March 2002 a small group of invited friends assembled beforehand at Ryeland Cottage to meet Anne Hopper and Doreen Parsons, the Mayor of Carlisle. It was a beautiful spring day and both Anne and Doreen were photographed holding day old lambs. Others present included Suzanne Greenhill and Nick Green from Heart of Cumbria, who must have found it a welcome change to attend a public event where he did not have to raise his voice.

We then proceeded to Rosehill where we were met by Trevor Hebden, the chief executive of Harrison and Hetherington, and also the Reverend Colin Randall, from the church next to my smallholding, who I had invited to say a prayer. Colin and his wife Judy had been very supportive to me throughout foot and mouth. Anne Hopper spoke movingly about the experience of the previous year before planting the weeping willow, with assistance from Doreen and Trevor Hebden.

Next to the weeping willow was placed a plaque which said, 'This tree was planted as a symbol of hope, a sign of new life, firmly planted for the future for all those who suffered during this 2001 foot & mouth epidemic.'

Colin blessed the tree and we all prayed fervently that it would thrive and serve as a constant reminder to future generations of what had happened to the people and animals of Cumbria.

The day after the ceremony I heard that the House of Lords had managed to halt the progress of the Animal Health Bill by voting not to consider it further until the government had completed consultation on the bill's proposed powers and the results of the three foot and mouth enquiries had been received.

I should have felt huge relief at this news. However, by then I was already facing a more pressing development at home, which posed an immediate threat to my flock.

13

LEAVING THE FIELD

One day at the beginning of March, I had been out giving my sheep their early morning feed, when I noticed three men standing at my gate looking at the eleven acre field behind the cottage. Surely they were not from DEFRA, I thought. They were not. One of the men turned out to be the estate manager of the landlord from whom I rented the field. The other two were organisers of the annual agricultural steam rally due to be held in May on the Down-a-Gate recreation ground, the end of which was opposite the cottage.

The previous year's rally had been cancelled because of foot and mouth restrictions but they were planning to go ahead as normal in 2002. What they wanted to know was whether or not I had any objection to my field being used for car parking on the day of the event.

I looked at them as if they were mad and, by the time I had finished shouting at them, they were in no doubt that I was mad - mad as hell. I pointed out to them that I had only just started lambing and would not have finished by the time of the rally. Where exactly did they think I could put all my sheep, including newly born lambs and expectant ewes, while the field was being used as a car park?

I reminded them that restrictions were still in force, because of concern that foot and mouth could recur at any time. Why else was the government so keen to see its Animal Health Bill become law? I was still required to have buckets of disinfectant at the entrance to my property and I was still unable to move any of my animals without first obtaining a licence from DEFRA. Finally, I did not like the idea of vehicles - many of which would come from farms - arriving from goodness knows where and being parked in my field, onto which I would be letting my sheep back to graze afterwards. After all I had been through in the previous twelve months, it was too much of a risk. I said that I would have to contact DEFRA and seek their advice. The three men beat a hasty retreat.

As soon as they had gone, I telephoned DEFRA and explained to one of the veterinary officers what had happened. He advised strongly against allowing the field to be used as a car park and agreed to confirm that advice in writing. As soon as I received his letter, I forwarded a copy to my landlord. That, I thought, should be the end of that. I could not have been more wrong.

I heard nothing more from the landlord until the Friday evening before the tree planting ceremony. I had just come in from the lambing shed to wash my hands when the telephone rang. It was a man who claimed to be an estate manager of the landlord, but he certainly was not the manager who had visited me earlier in the month. This man told me that no grass lettings had been made in the current year and therefore I should not be using the field. I was required to take all of my sheep off the field by nine o'clock the next morning or else steps would have to be taken to remove them.

I was stunned. When I had collected myself, I told him that I was doing absolutely nothing until I had spoken to the landlord's solicitors. It was usually they who dealt with any matters concerning the field including my rent, the latest installment of which I had only paid them a few weeks ago. I pointed out that I had nowhere else to move my sheep and anyway I could not do so without first obtaining a licence from DEFRA.

The caller was unmoved. He insisted I remove all of my sheep by the next morning. I put the telephone down.

I could not believe this. It was like a bad dream. Moving my sheep was out of the question, but what steps would be taken if I did not? I imagined a gang of men arriving with lorries to cart off my sheep to an undisclosed destination so that the landlord could reclaim his field. Yet again I telephoned DEFRA. I knew someone would be there, as the telephone was being manned 24 hours a day in case of any fresh outbreaks of suspected foot and mouth. The official on duty told me not to worry. If anyone turned up the following day to try any bullying tactics about my sheep, I should call their office and someone from DEFRA would come straight out to my property to intervene.

I reflected on how ironic it was that, after all the months of battling against MAFF and DEFRA over my flock, I should now be turning to them for protection against a new and unexpected threat towards my sheep.

Despite the assurance from DEFRA, I spent the weekend in a state of high anxiety and I was never more grateful for having Holly, the dober-man cross. She could not believe her luck as I allowed her to patrol up and down the path to the cottage as much as she wanted and to bark her head off at any passing person or vehicle.

It was all very puzzling. I had rented the field under an annual agree-ment since October 1998 with rent payable twice yearly in March and August. There had never been any problems before. On the contrary, the landlord and his staff had always been most helpful. On the only occa-sion when I had had difficulty over paying the rent in August 2001, as a result of hardship from the foot and mouth restrictions, it had been agreed that I could spread this over four monthly installments. But I had paid the rent due for March 2002 on time and I knew that the cheque had been cashed.

It was true, now I came to think of it, that the landlord's solicitors had not sent me a new annual agreement for the tenancy of the field but then, on at least two previous occasions, the new agreement had not been issued until some time after the old one had lapsed. Anyway, I reasoned, if there was a problem over my continuing tenancy, surely there would have been no need for the first estate manager to come down and ask if I had any objection to the field being used for a car park during the steam rally?

The weekend passed without incident and as soon as possible on Monday I telephoned the landlord's solicitors. I was sure it would be possible to resolve the matter reasonably. But no one was available and I waited in vain to have my telephone message returned. Tuesday was the day of the tree planting ceremony and I decided I was not going to allow the uncertainty over the field and my sheep to spoil that occasion. Wednesday brought the bombshell in the form of a letter from the land-lord's solicitors.

They were instructed that the landlord did not wish to enter into an agreement over the field and asked me to vacate the land by the end of the month, otherwise the landlord 'would be obliged to take action to recover possession.' The solicitors acknowledged that they had received a payment of rent from me on 1 March but argued that the period cov-ered by this had now expired, apparently overlooking the fact that the first six month period of each annual agreement ended on 30 April.

I was flabbergasted. It was one thing to have a telephone call out of the blue from someone claiming to be the landlord's estate manager and insisting I must vacate the field at once. It was quite another to receive a letter from a leading firm of Carlisle solicitors telling me the same thing. Clearly I was going to have to consult a solicitor myself.

I was put in touch with Hexham solicitor Geoffrey Ridley, who attempted to reason in correspondence with the landlord's solicitors. He argued that, in the circumstances, I should be allowed to continue in occupation of the field until the end of October, when any new annual agreement would have expired. This would enable me to complete lambing and be able to dispose of my livestock at auction in the autumn. It was pointed out that I had nowhere else immediately available to move my sheep and that, as a result of foot and mouth restrictions, these numbered many more than normal. Indeed, by the end of lambing, I had more than seventy sheep, including lambs, which was far more than I had ever had or had ever intended to have.

The request, that I be allowed to stay until the end of October, was rejected and the landlord's solicitors continued to insist that I vacate the field immediately. Reason was clearly not going to prevail and it looked as if we were headed for litigation. Geoffrey advised that a litigation specialist was needed and referred me to his fellow Hexham solicitor, Peter Jewitt. After consultation, Peter wrote to the landlord's solicitors asking that I be allowed to stay only until the end of June, so as to complete lambing and arrange for the sheep to be moved elsewhere. This request was rejected also and was followed by the issue of a summons requiring my vacation of the field within 30 days, which in practice gave me to the middle of June.

By now I had decided that, in view of the obdurate stance taken by the landlord, there was little point in contesting the issue. I did not have the money to fight a legal battle whereas I knew this was not a consideration for the landlord. But even if I had, I no longer wished to stay on the field after the way in which I had been treated.

Peter Jewitt advised that the most cost effective approach would be to ask the court to make a suspended possession order, with possession being suspended until 30 June, i.e. the date which we had already proposed in correspondence. He thought the court would consider this reasonable in the circumstances, particularly since at no time had the landlord indicated why it was now suddenly so urgent to reclaim the field.

In the meantime, I had been getting on with the business of 'downsizing' my flock. The Blackies all went to a sale for ewes with lambs at foot, so that I knew whoever bought them would keep them for another year. The other crossbreeds were advertised on my website and by word of mouth. They and their lambs all found good homes with a variety of smallholders. Having put up a fight to keep them alive during foot and mouth, I could not possibly send any of them for slaughter. I kept the trading standards office very busy with requests for movement licences.

I had worried especially that no one would be willing to take Fiver the bald Leicester, who I was convinced had been crossed with a goat. But I was lucky or, I should say, she was lucky. I heard about a philanthropist quite nearby who had a private animal sanctuary, where animals were allowed to die naturally of old age. I contacted the estate manager and told him about Fiver. He must have been intrigued because he agreed to come out to see her the following day.

When he did, I explained how, because of her lack of wool, she had one coat for the summer and another for the winter. He looked dubious. I added that she was in lamb. Quite reasonably, the manager asked if all of Fiver's lambs came out like her, without any wool. I think he had visions of a flock of baby Fivers (or perhaps that should be 'one pounders') all running about in little jackets. No, I assured him, Fiver always had big but normal lambs and usually three of them. To prove this, I showed him pictures of lambs from past years. He looked greatly relieved and it was agreed that she would go to the sanctuary in the following week.

The morning before Fiver was due to be collected I went into the shed to feed her. I had been keeping her in at night in case it rained and also because with her out of the way I could feed sheep in the field, without having to worry that Fiver would collar the lot and pig out. She was lying in the shed, moaning and groaning. Oh no, I thought, bloat again. I followed the vet's advice from previous such episodes and got Fiver to her feet and outside. Then I made her walk up and down. Each time she stopped, I made her walk on.

Robert Crozier was calling by that morning to do some foot trimming and I was pleased when I saw his car arrive. He asked what I was doing.

'Fiver's got bloat again,' I said.

'I don't think so, Moira', replied Robert, 'I think she wants to lamb'.

We went back into the shed and Robert took over. Half an hour later, Robert decided Fiver needed some help. Having applied lambing oil, he gave her an internal examination and remarked that he could feel one big head. Then he began to pull and pull. At last, one big head and two long legs appeared.

'My goodness,' exclaimed Robert, 'this is a big one.'

Robert continued to pull and Fiver continued to groan. At last the body appeared. What a length. It seemed to go on forever. It was more like a two week old lamb than a first day lamb.

'Wow,' said Robert, 'that is the biggest one I have ever delivered in my life.'

Poor Fiver was exhausted. So Robert and I saw to the lamb before leaving it with Fiver and going indoors to have a coffee and to recover from the shock of this outsize special delivery.

I contacted the estate manager to tell him what had happened and we agreed he should postpone the collection for a while. Then I telephoned Susan Bull and asked if she had any baby scales left from her days on the district. She had. They were solid brass. Well, you would expect nothing less from Susan. I collected these from her and when I got home I placed the lamb in a pillowcase and put it on the scales.

It weighed in at just over sixteen pounds, compared to a normal lamb, which weighs typically in the region of six pounds. I contacted my friends at the *Cumberland News* and they were out the same day to take pictures of Fiver and her big baby lamb.

A photograph followed in the *News & Star* under the heading 'Moira had a little lamb - and one that weighed sixteen pounds.' Readers were invited to telephone the newspaper with the weight of any larger newly born lamb. But apparently no one did.

I kept them at home for another three weeks before they were taken away to the sanctuary, where I know they are both well cared for. I am told the lamb is now as big as Fiver but it is white and has a good fleece, unlike her mother.

By the time of the court hearing all of my sheep had gone to new homes apart from Topsy and the Ryelands plus their lambs, which I was determined to keep although where I did not know. The paddocks on my

own bit of land around the cottage were not large enough to accommodate all of them during the summer. I thought I had found a suitable field
in Aglionby that I could let and which had the advantage of being near
enough to enable me to visit the sheep at least once a day to check on
them, without having to travel very far. Unfortunately the field had
clumps of ragwort, which is poisonous to animals, so that was the end of
that.

One evening I received a call from a friend, Marie, who had been on
the same computer class as me. She had heard of my plight and told me
she had a large paddock at the back of her house, which I was welcome
to use for the rest of the year and at no charge. She lived seven miles
away at Talkin and I went to visit the next day. It was the most beautiful
spot high up overlooking Talkin Tarn. There was a running stream at the
end of the paddock and I knew that the sheep would be well looked after
by Marie, as she is such an animal lover.

I attended the county court in Carlisle with Peter Jewitt on 12 June.
The hearing was before Deputy District Judge Rachel Eaton and was
held in her private chambers. Having heard both sides of the argument,
she decided that I should be allowed to continue in occupation of the field
until the end of June and that I should pay rent for what was in effect the
two months of May and June. Claims by the landlord's solicitor for
immediate possession of the field and an award of additional costs were
rejected. I felt that I had achieved a victory of a kind although I derived
little pleasure from the result.

Unsurprisingly the local press got hold of the story and a big article
appeared in the *News & Star* along the lines of 'Smallholder told to quit',
accompanied by the famous foot and mouth photograph of me in my
woolly hat clutching a Ryeland lamb. Unfortunately, the article was not
entirely accurate and I had to write a letter correcting several points of
detail. In particular, the impression was given misleadingly that I personally was being made homeless, as well as my sheep. Fortunately it
was only the field that the landlord owned. The cottage was most definitely mine.

The paper published the full text of my letter which I ended as follows:
'I am deeply saddened by the events of the last few weeks, which have
resulted in the effective destruction of my smallholding.'

That was that. From my landing window, I looked out on a field that only a year ago had been a potential battleground during the height of the foot and mouth crisis. Now it was as barren as it would have been had my sheep succumbed to disease or I had succumbed to MAFF's voluntary cull. Where both foot and mouth and MAFF had failed, the landlord had succeeded.

14

THE FINAL TEST

Before I could move Topsy and the Ryelands to Marie's at Talkin village, they all had to have their ears tagged with my agricultural holding number. Some of the ears festered and I had to get my vet to cut the tags out.

'Mind, I will have to tag the other ear on each of them, Moira,' said Jonathan, 'DEFRA rules you know.'

'Not blooming likely,' I replied.

'Well,' laughed Jonathan, 'no doubt you will tell DEFRA where to go, if they call to carry out a spot check. By the way, did you know they call you the Rottweiler?'

I was quite taken aback but decided that I would treat this as a compliment, although it was probably not intended as one.

Topsy and the Ryelands settled in well at their temporary new home and I went up most days to see them and check that none had got fly strike. This is a nasty condition for sheep, because maggots appear within hours and can drive them to distraction. The maggots need to be eradicated as soon as possible. However, Marie's field had the advantage of being on high ground so that the sheep had a trouble free summer residing there.

The only two sheep that I kept behind at Ryeland Cottage, in one of the paddocks on my own land, were the two promised to Prince Charles - Harry and Amanda Jane. I was hoping and expecting that they would be able to go to Highgrove in the next few weeks, although I realised the move might be delayed as I knew that the farm manager there would wish to make doubly certain that he was not bringing any chance of disease on to the estate.

After the last year, it seemed very strange coming out of the cottage to find just two sheep grazing, although with the dogs, geese and hens, there was no lack of accompanying noise.

In general, things were at last beginning to settle down in the country but there were still restrictions in place. For example, all farmers had to continue to observe a 20 day standstill following the movement of any livestock. This meant that, if you brought a new animal onto your land, you could not move any other animal in or out for the next 20 days afterwards. This did not make any difference to me. Movement of my sheep between Warwick Bridge and Talkin was classified as happening on the same holding. But it made life difficult for commercial farmers.

Of more impact for me was the fact that it was taking time for the agricultural shows to get back to normal. In 2001 these had all been cancelled because of foot and mouth but in 2002 many of them imposed limitations on entries. For example, I had hoped to enter Mr Universe for the Royal Highland Show, but the organisers decided that they would not accept any sheep from south of the border. The Cumberland Show went even further, quite understandably, in banning livestock altogether. I thought about entering him for the Great Yorkshire Show at Harrogate but after giving it a great deal of thought I decided to err on the side of caution and did not apply. So, for the second summer running, I did not attend any shows with Mr Universe.

In July 2002 two of the three inquiries set up by the government published their reports in quick succession. These were the Royal Society's Inquiry into the handling of animal diseases and an inquiry headed by Dr Iain Anderson into the administrative handling of the crisis, which had come to be known as the Lessons Learned Inquiry. The other inquiry on the future of farming had reported already in January.

The Royal Society's Inquiry, chaired by Sir Brian Follett, came down strongly in support of vaccination as part of any strategy to control a future outbreak of foot and mouth in the United Kingdom. It continued to favour the culling of infected animals and known dangerous contacts, together with the implementation of movement controls, but suggested that healthy animals on neighbouring premises should be vaccinated as a 'major tool of first resort' to prevent the disease spreading.

This was the complete opposite to the government's approach during 2001. Then, vaccination, while often raised as an option under consideration, was nevertheless presented very much as a minor tool of last resort.

But the report also stressed the old adage that prevention was better than cure. 'The overall objective of policy must be to minimise the risk of a disease entering the country. It is essential that the UK, and the European Union, strengthen their early warning systems and ensure that warnings are acted upon. Import controls over meat products require tightening.'

This, I felt, was the core argument. I had read only recently in the newspapers that illegal meat products were entering British airports on a daily basis in containers and passengers' suitcases and that to combat this, two (yes, two) dogs had been trained especially to sniff out luggage. In a fury and I suppose with a little more time on my hands now that I had less animals to look after, I had dashed off a letter on this very topic to the *Newcastle Journal*, which it published:

'Sir, After all this country went through last year it will take a long time for farming to get back to anything that can be considered normal.

'I and many others would like to know what the EU will do to make our government take seriously the threat of FMD coming into this country again.

'Farmers are tied by restrictions with the 20 day standstill. County shows, auction marts and rare breed sales are dying because of the biosecurity rules imposed upon us and what does this government do?

'We have two dogs to detect illegal meat entering this country. This is as much use as having two footbaths in the whole of Cumbria to keep the county safe in a foot and mouth epidemic.

'We farmers are doing all we are told to do to keep the disease out. I would like to see action taken against the government if FMD enters this country through negligence on their part.

'Farmers are sick and tired of being blamed for government inadequacies and we are not prepared to go through the horrors and hardships of 2001 again.'

I read later that there had since been a 50 per cent reduction to the sniffer dog complement. One of the dogs was reported to be off sick. It had cocked its leg over an item of luggage on a conveyor belt and received such an electrical shock that it now refused to work.

The Lessons Learned Inquiry had conducted a series of two day meetings around the country to hear, at first hand, accounts from those areas most affected by the outbreak of foot and mouth. One of the meetings had been at the Shepherds Inn in March, the scene of so many meetings at the height of the crisis, which I had attended, along with many other friends from the previous year's campaigns.

The chairman, Dr Iain Anderson, had opened by saying that he was 'very conscious of the scale of the outbreak in Cumbria' and emphasised that 'this is your meeting and we are here to listen.' And that is just what he did. One after another speakers came forward including Suzanne and Peter Greenhill, Nick Green, Ellie Logan of SAD and David Parker from Longtown (a former barrister and frequent writer of letters to the press).

I also spoke, choosing to draw attention to how I had resisted having ministry vets come on to my property for fear that they would subsequently be found to be 'dirty' and pointing out that the ones who kept their animals received no compensation.

At the end of the meeting, Dr Anderson said that he appreciated the transparency and honesty expressed that evening. He felt the meeting had been somewhat different to others held. 'Your accounts have closed the gap between us considerably,' he said. He could appreciate what had happened in Cumbria. The 'residual anger and frustration had made an impact.'

The report finally produced by the Lessons Learned Inquiry joined the Royal Society in supporting vaccination as part of a future strategy for containing foot and mouth and vaccination to live rather than vaccination to kill. It highlighted government failures to prepare for such an outbreak and in the handling of the initial stages, particularly the delay in bringing in the Army in Cumbria and Devon. It found that former Agriculture Minister Nick Brown had lost public confidence by claiming that the disease was under control when it was palpably not. It came down strongly against burning animals on mass pyres as a means for disposing of infected animals.

In responding to the report on behalf of the government, Mrs Beckett, Nick Brown's successor, acknowledged that 'mistakes were bound to have been made,' as if there was a degree of inevitability about the way the crisis had developed. I did not agree. Nor was I totally convinced by her assurance that vaccination would form part of the government's strategy for containing the disease in the event of another outbreak.

To coincide with the Lessons Learned Inquiry report, the BBC interviewed Brigadier Alex Birtwistle, now in retirement and free to express his views on the situation that he had found in March 2001: 'It's not so much that we were brought in late but that it wasn't necessary for us to be brought in at all - it should have been a simple main task... It was a hell of a mess by the time we were brought in. There were rotting heaps of carcasses which had been outside people's houses for about three weeks... We're one of the ten richest nations, we're a legitimate nuclear power and we can't get a few trucks into Cumbria.'

In the same interview he denied that farmers had encouraged the disease to rage out of control by breaking bio-security measures. 'The great majority of farmers behaved terribly well,' he said. 'A few people did carry out inadequate bio-security - but not necessarily farmers.'

As far as I was concerned, I knew what the Brigadier meant. He did not have to spell it out.

Before summer drew to a close, I started to look for a small field nearer to Warwick Bridge, as I knew Marie would soon be expecting me to take my sheep away from Talkin. Robert Crozier came to trim the ewes' feet and said that he might have found me the perfect place for my sheep, only two miles away at Crosby-on-Eden.

It belonged to an old family friend, Margaret Brown. She had bred pedigree Suffolk sheep but unfortunately her stock had been taken out under the three kilometre cull. Not that her sheep had had foot and mouth. But, surrounded by other farms with cattle, she had felt she had no choice other than to let her sheep go, although it had broken her heart to do so. Robert told me that Margaret had a small paddock adjoining her house and garden, which might be just what I was looking for. He gave me Margaret's telephone number. I rang her later that day and set off at once to call on her.

As I turned off the road and onto Margaret's long drive, the first thing I noticed on my left was the paddock, which Robert had mentioned. The second thing I noticed, as I neared the house, was the most beautiful garden. It was just like something out of a gardening magazine. I half expected Alan Titchmarsh to jump out from behind a bush. Then, as I turned the corner to the front of her house, I noticed a collection of outbuildings to my right and in front with another field beyond.

This looks an ideal spot for my sheep, I thought to myself. Not only was there a paddock and another field so that you could change sheep around or keep one part of the flock separate from another, but also there was a shed that could be used for lambing. It did not take me long to conclude that Margaret was also the ideal person to have temporary custody of my sheep. She was clearly very fond of animals and still scarred by the loss of her Suffolks. All she had left were a few hens and a big friendly dog called Beth Brown. It was agreed that I would move my sheep down from Talkin to Crosby-on-Eden in the autumn and when the time came they all settled in to their latest new home.

The National Scrapie Plan was still ticking along and I received a letter from the Rare Breeds Survival Trust asking me to take part in a special programme. I did not want to take part and was surprised and annoyed that my private test results of the previous year for the two rams did not appear to count for anything. However, because I planned to attend shows the next year with my sheep and all the other Ryeland breeders were having their flocks done I felt obliged to participate.

I was decidedly unhappy to discover that the whole flock had to be tested and that, in addition to giving blood samples, each poor sheep had to be fitted with an electronic bolus which was fired into the stomach and remained in place for the rest of the animal's life. Moreover, this time I had to accept that someone from DEFRA would have to carry out the tests. I could not use my own vet.

I knew I would need a competent sheep handler to hold each animal for the DEFRA vet and I asked Robert if he could come and do the necessary on the day. I also asked my artist friend, Liz, if she could come round and record the proceedings on video. If anything went wrong as a result of DEFRA incompetence, I wanted to make sure that the evidence had been captured on camera.

The day arrived for the scrapie testing. Liz, Robert and I were all ready when the vet from DEFRA turned up. After my one and only experience of a male DEFRA vet, I was pleased to find that this one was a woman. In fact it turned out that she was not a vet but an animal inspector. I guessed that she must have drawn the short straw to be the one coming out to visit me. I still had the road sign on the chain across the entrance to my main gate that said 'MAFF OFF MY SHEEP' and I noticed her looking at it, as I went out to open the gate for her to come on to the drive.

I had had to bring all of the sheep across from Margaret's at Crosby-on-Eden and pen them inside the shed. Liz had already begun to video the proceedings when the inspector produced a bolus from her box of tricks that was a good four inches in length. I was stunned and thought there was no way that it would be possible to slide such an object down the short neck of a Ryeland. Robert thought the same and spoke up.

'No,' he said to the inspector, 'you cannot use that!'

The inspector agreed and produced a slightly smaller one, which Robert and I said was okay. Then, just as she was about to begin taking blood from the first animal, she looked at Liz.

'Are you filming?' she asked, 'I am afraid I will have to ask you to stop before I begin, as DEFRA does not allow filming.'

I must admit that this inspector knew how to take blood and she managed to do so and administer the boluses without causing stress to any of the animals. The only problem she had was with the bolus for Mr Universe. The thing got stuck in his throat. It would have to be him of course. The inspector had a small machine, which could track the journey of the bolus from the sheep's mouth right down until it stopped in the lower stomach. She said that she would go back to him later. So I gave him a couple of digestive biscuits to help move it. When she scanned Mr Universe later, the bolus had gone to where it was supposed to go.

When the inspector had finished with all the sheep, I invited her inside for a cup of coffee with Liz and Robert. In the middle of the conversation Robert suddenly piped up.

'Well, what do you think now you have met the Rottweiler?'

I cringed with embarrassment. The inspector blushed and smiled and said she had heard I did not like DEFRA. We spent quite some time chatting about the foot and mouth outbreak and I sensed that she was not altogether happy with everything that had happened.

As with my private test from the autumn before, I had to wait a month for the results to come back. But when they did, all of my sheep were confirmed as ARR/ARR and therefore about as unsusceptible to scrapie as it was possible to be. So far as I was concerned, this was the final test for my Ryelands and they had passed it with flying colours.

15

THE HIGH ROAD

The scrapie testing was carried out in October 2002 and by this time the Animal Health Bill, whose passage had been brought to a halt in March, was in the process of being re-introduced with some amendments. In particular a 'vaccinate to live' policy had been inserted to apply to premises where no infection had been detected. The Secretary of State was required to give priority to vaccination in such circumstances. There was also to be a right of appeal against the new power of entry onto land. It was provided that a warrant could not be issued unless the landholder had first had an opportunity to contest the application before a magistrate.

In the course of re-introducing the bill in the House of Lords, DEFRA minister Lord Whitty was surprisingly explicit on the dubious legality of MAFF's actions during the 2001 outbreak with regard to the contiguous cull, 'The bill addresses gaps in the powers of the government. We are dealing here with powers that we do not currently have. One such power is the power of preventative slaughter. That is what the clause is about. It is intended to give us that power which we lacked and which we would need in a future outbreak.'

I mulled over those words. 'Gaps in the powers of government... powers that we do not currently have... it is intended to give us that power which we lacked and which we would need in a future outbreak.'

Here, so far as I was concerned, was absolute confirmation from the government itself that a central part of MAFF's culling policy during 2001, which I had regarded anyway as wholly unjustifiable, had in fact no legal basis whatsoever.

The bill received Royal Assent on 7 November 2002 and the 2002 Animal Health Act was on the statute book. Despite the amendments, there could be no doubting that the overall effect was to strengthen immeasurably the powers of the government. In the event of another outbreak of foot and mouth, I reflected that the battle would be harder to fight next time round.

By now I was in regular contact with the farm manager at Highgrove about arrangements for Harry and Amanda Jane to make the long awaited move south to Gloucestershire. They would be going from a holding of one acre to a farm with more than a thousand acres, although I did not suppose for a moment that they would be given the run of all of these.

A date was agreed for late November and in advance of this the news was released to the media. It was yet another opportunity for the press to reproduce the notorious 'woolly hat photograph', but this time with ample justification since the lamb pictured was indeed Harry.

Harry and Amanda Jane would not be travelling alone because, much to my delight, Amanda Jane was in lamb. Not only were Ryelands being reintroduced to royalty after the days of King George III but also there would be a royal birth to celebrate in the near future. I hoped that it would be the first of many and the start of a royal Ryeland flock to add to the many other rare and native breeds of sheep, cattle and pigs that the Prince of Wales keeps on his farm.

On 24 November 2002, the farm manager, David Wilson, arrived with his wife to collect Harry and Amanda Jane for the long journey to Highgrove. I was sad to see them go but I felt proud at the same time. I knew they would be going to a good home.

Not long after, I received a lovely letter from His Royal Highness thanking me for the two lambs and commenting on the wonderful fleece that Ryelands had and how perfect this was for spinners. He had given strict instructions for Harry and Amanda Jane to be given special attention and added that he would be keeping a close eye on them himself.

David Wilson told me later that both Harry and Amanda Jane had settled in very well and he hoped I would be able to visit them in their new home before very long.

One of my e-mail friends, Yvonne Sparkes, was moved to verse by the occasion:

> *Moira had a little lamb.*
> *Young Harry was his name.*
> *Hiding from those government men*
> *Was how Harry found his fame.*
> *A barricaded home had he*
> *To save him from his fate,*

While Moira would his case then plead,
And try to hope and wait.
She sought the very top for help
And, much to her surprise,
A princely letter of support
Appeared before her eyes.
Those times were hard and people lost
Their flocks and stock were gone.
Yet battling Moira, now refreshed
With hope, just carried on.
The press and media too were there.
Those photos did them proud,
As little Harry blinked and sighed
And bleated rather loud.
Now when this awful day had passed
And everything was safe,
A gift of these two Ryeland sheep
To the Prince our Moira gave.
So now they are established,
With the hope they will remain.
Moira's loss is nothing
To the Prince and Highgrove's gain.
A rich and ancient heritage,
With a breed of noble birth,
Deserving this the finest stage,
A place on royal earth.
They are on view, and proud to be,
For all who come and tarry
To admire and pet those lovely sheep,
Amanda Jane and our young Harry.
So much was given out of love.
For the animals she would fight.
And now to see those lovely sheep,
We just know that Moira's right.

Leaving aside the famous nursery rhyme about Mary's little lamb, I do not know of any other individual sheep that can claim to have had a poem written about him or her. Perhaps one day someone will pen a few lines about Mr Universe.

Harry and Amanda Jane's departure meant that I had some free space in my paddocks at the cottage so that I could bring back the occasional sheep from Margaret's at Crosby-on-Eden for any treatment that might be needed. As a general rule, only Mr Universe was a permanent resident. Titan, Topsy and the Ryeland ewes were based at Margaret's. I did the trip back and forth to Crosby so often I felt I could have driven blindfolded.

I had three New Year wishes for 2003. The first was for some healthy and strong Ryeland lambs, preferably ewes. The second was to take Mr Universe at long last to the Royal Highland Show. The third was to have a peaceful and uneventful year. As things turned out, I got one and a bit wishes granted.

The only Ryeland to lamb was Sophie and she had just the one, a ram that I called Robbie - not, I hasten to add, after Robbie Williams, but after Robert Crozier. I could tell from little Robbie's back legs that Mr Universe was the father. For the first time ever Topsy, who could usually be relied on for three lambs, did not have any.

Initially I kept Sophie and Robbie in one field at Margaret's and put Topsy and the remaining Ryeland ewes in the other. Titan came back to the cottage and went into one of the paddocks from where he would stand and glower at Mr Universe through the fence and across the path that kept them apart. The two old rams, which had been such good friends in their younger days, now had to be separated to prevent a fight breaking out. However, Mr Universe at least did not lack for female company. His paddock, which was the larger of the two, was frequented by the geese, Jemima and Eric, both of which seemed very fond of him. Jemima, in particular, would cuddle up to Mr Universe whenever he was sitting down, which was more often than not.

Mr Universe and the geese shared a common taste for salad food. All three were very partial to lettuce and the geese were keen also on slices of cucumber. Mr Universe liked so many different things that in the end I had devised a 'Ryeland salad' for his consumption. Celery, carrot, apple and lettuce all chopped up and mixed together in a bowl. A healthy change, I thought, from digestive biscuits.

Apart from Robbie, the only other lamb to which I could lay claim was the one born to Harry and Amanda Jane at Highgrove. I received the news in a call from the shepherd there, who told me that it was a ewe and how much he was enjoying looking after them all. I had hoped to pay them a visit, along with Suzanne and Peter Greenhill, but maddeningly I had developed a 'frozen shoulder' and was in such discomfort that I did not relish a long car journey. It was all I could do to manage the short trip back and forth to Crosby.

Given the state I was in, it was perhaps just as well that Robbie was the only lamb that I had to look after, although it was sad that he did not have any other little companions to run about with. After a few weeks, I let Sophie and Robbie join Topsy and the other Ryeland ewes. It was hilarious to watch Robbie's confusion as he rushed in turn to the other Ryelands, each of whom told him where to go in no uncertain manner, before he linked up again with his mother. I wondered if being brought up alone with only a mother and several aunts would affect his psychological development in any way.

I tried various treatments for my shoulder but in the end it seemed that the only cure was to give it time and plenty of rest, neither of which I had. I was hoping that this year the agricultural shows would finally be back to normal and I obtained membership of the Royal Highland Agricultural Society so as to be able to enter Mr Universe and Titan for the Royal Highland Show in the summer. I felt that, after all these two had been through, they deserved the opportunity to appear at such a prestigious event and I was determined that nothing was going to stop me from attending.

I wrote to the *Journal* in search of sponsorship and ended up with sponsorship from the paper itself and the Cumberland Building Society. I also received a generous contribution from one of my e-mail friends Mary-June in the United States and a limited edition print from Newcastle United, signed by Bobby Robson and Alan Shearer, that I could auction.

However, to my dismay, Mr Universe had developed a pressure sore on his chest and I was having the devil's own job getting it to clear up. It was also a problem trying to keep the treated area clean and poor Mr Universe ended up wearing a harness made out of bandages tied behind his neck in an effort to hold everything in place. It was quite a performance to change these on my own and I was grateful that two nursing friends, Moira and her sister Anne, would often come across from

Newcastle on their days off to give a professional helping hand. Passers by must have wondered what on earth was going on at the sight of Mr Universe in the paddock, looking a little like Winnie-the-Pooh with his shrunken vest in the House at Pooh Corner.

I was concerned that Mr Universe would not recover in time for the Royal Highland Show but my concern over him was as nothing to the worry about my father's declining state of health. He had been rushed into South Tyneside Hospital and after various tests it had been found that cancer, for which he had been operated some time before, had returned. He had told the doctors that on no account were they to operate again. He was ninety and enough was enough.

Having made arrangements for all the animals, I drove across to see him. I had always felt that he and I had a special bond. I had learnt so much from him as a child. He was immensely practical, very much the perfectionist, always active, determined to finish whatever he set out to do and a great lover of animals. If the men from MAFF had ever encountered him in his prime they would have had no difficulty in making the family connection, particularly as he was about my height.

Sitting up in the hospital bed, he looked a shadow of his former self, but whatever his physical state, his brain was still sharp.

'Moira, pet,' he said, 'I wish you weren't so far way. Will you come back home? I would die happy knowing you were back nearer to your mother.'

What could I say? What could I do? I had been in Cumbria for seven years. I had made many friends and I had made a new life. But ever since the business of losing the field behind the cottage and being separated from most of my sheep on a day to day basis as a result I had been thinking about the possibility of moving.

So I looked my father in the eye and promised him I would do what he wished as soon as possible. He relaxed visibly. He knew that I would keep my word.

I drove back from Tyneside with all manner of thoughts racing through my mind. Selling the cottage was the least of my problems, as I knew that once on the market it would attract a lot of interest. I also had somewhere in Newcastle to which I could go with the dogs and cat. But although this house had a sizeable garden, there was no land for sheep or, for that matter, geese and hens. What to do about them?

Yet again I turned to the press for help. I contacted the *Journal* in Newcastle and they published a piece about my planned return to the north east and a search for a new but temporary home for my sheep, until I got myself sorted out. After a great deal of thought, I had decided that I could give up my two geese and the hens but that I could not say good-bye to Mr Universe, Titan, Topsy and the Ryelands. I might have to leave the River Eden behind but I was definitely not leaving the Eden Flock behind. They were coming with me, even though we might have to be separated for a while.

I was inundated with calls in response to the piece in the *Journal* but one call seemed particularly promising. This was from Tony Walton, the manager at Gibside, an estate owned by the National Trust. He said that he was sure Suzanne and John Gibson could accommodate the sheep on their farm at Gibside for as long as I needed and would keep an eye on them. I do not know if Tony had looked at my website before contacting me and seen the reference to the Prince of Wales and Harry and Amanda Jane. Ironically, Gibside had been the family home of none other than his grandmother, Elizabeth, the Queen Mother, and Prince Charles, I learnt, had just agreed to become patron of Gibside.

With arrangements made for the sheep, I was able to concentrate on treating Mr Universe and trying to get him ready for the Highland Show, as well as preparing the cottage for being put up for sale, continuing my daily trips to Crosby and, when I could, driving across again to Tyneside to see my father. Having come home from hospital, he had now gone into a hospice and I knew he did not have long.

Even so, when he died it was still a shock. I tried to comfort myself with the thought that, unlike Stephen three years earlier, I had at least been able to see him before he died and tell him how much I loved him - and that I was complying with his final wish by moving back to the north east.

The funeral was held at South Shields crematorium. A lady vicar conducted the service. I do not know whether or not my father would have approved of this. However, I knew he would have approved of the musical accompaniment to the disappearance from view of his coffin, because it was at his specific request. It was Frank Sinatra singing *My Way*.

Someone else who had always done things very much her way was now causing me worry. Susan Bull had been having difficulty with her breathing and altogether was in a bad way. She had been told that she needed to have an operation but that it was touch and go whether or not it would be successful, given her condition. Against that, without the operation it was apparently only a matter of time before her system would pack up and so Susan had decided to go for it.

Ever since the start of the foot and mouth crisis, hardly a day had passed without Susan and me speaking on the telephone, usually at night. I spoke to her the evening before she was due to go into the Cumberland Infirmary.

'Susan,' I said, 'I'm worried about this operation.'

'Don't you worry,' was her riposte, 'I'm a fighter. They won't get rid of me that easily.'

She had been reading Claire Tomalin's recent biography of Samuel Pepys and pronounced herself amazed at some of the things that Pepys had got up to. She was talking of writing her own memoirs except, she said, that they would have to be kept private because of all the things she had got up to. She wished me luck for the Highland Show, which was fast approaching, and hoped that Mr Universe would be fit in time.

He was. All the time and attention lavished on him paid off and, having hired an aluminium trailer (wooden trailers were specifically prohibited because of the risk that they might harbour infection), I set off alone on the high road to Scotland with Mr Universe in tow. Because I was going on my own, I had decided against taking Titan as well. I could not risk the two of them getting into a fight and, although my frozen shoulder was improving, I knew I was going to have a hard enough job controlling one ram without worrying about another.

The Royal Highland Show is at Ingliston, near Edinburgh Airport and is a major event. The show's rules required its entrants and their animals to stay for the duration, which meant that I had to spend four days there with Mr Universe, even though the sheep judging would take place on the very first day of the show and there would be nothing further required thereafter.

I had bought a small tent, which I had practised at home putting up and taking down. However, I still needed a helping hand when I got to the show site. Mr Universe had a pen to himself. He did not look very happy. At least it was not raining.

The next morning we were on show early. The strength of the competition was daunting. I had never been to a show where there had been such high quality sheep on display. We were clearly in the Premier League here, I thought. The majority of the Ryeland rams were evidently much younger than Mr Universe, being only one or two years old.

In the end it was age that told against Mr Universe. The judge awarded him fourth place, which meant that I, or I should say he, still got a splendid rosette and a cash prize for the grand sum of £12. Afterwards, when all the Ryeland owners were relaxing together over a drink, the judge came across and told me that he could find absolutely no fault with Mr Universe's condition. It was simply a case of some of the younger rams moving more sprightly in the ring. Mr Universe was more on the sedate side. A year and certainly two years earlier it would have been very different. As it was, I was very pleased that Mr Universe had acquitted himself so well and felt that all the effort of getting him to the show had been vindicated.

One of the pleasures of the Royal Highland was the opportunity to meet up again with Susan Bryden and her father. They were delighted to see Mr Universe in such fine form and I was equally pleased that they had been able to restock with Ryelands, after the awful experience of losing all of their animals in 2001. Susan and her father had collected several first places with the new members of the Broomwell flock.

Mr Universe did not find the show such a pleasure. As the days wore on, he got more and more fed up being stuck in his pen. In the evenings, I would take him out for a walk on his lead so that he could get a little exercise and a change of scene. As it happened, my pleasure was marred by an accident with my glasses. I dropped these on the ground and, before I could pick them up, someone else trod on them. I did not have a spare pair and I knew they would be expensive to replace.

I was pleased when the time came to leave for home and Mr Universe even more so. I do not think driving without my glasses had anything to do with it because I would have been just as likely to do this if I had been wearing them but, in any event, I took a wrong turn on the way back and so the journey from Scotland was longer than it should have been. When we finally got back at dead of night, I let Mr Universe out of his trailer and into his paddock. He was overjoyed. I wished the judge could have seen his movement at that point. There was nothing sedate about it as he charged across the grass.

Susan Bull had had her operation shortly before I departed for the show and was still in the Infirmary when I returned. The signs were not hopeful according to Liz Gwyther, who had been going in to see Susan while I was away. I planned to go in to see her myself as soon as I could but I was too late. She died in the small hours.

In the space of a few weeks I had lost two people very dear to me in their very different ways. The first had been a constant support when I was a child and a teenager. The second had been no less constant in her support at a time of enormous stress and strain. Both of them had a never say die attitude to life and now both of them had set off on their own high road from this life to the next.

Susan's funeral was at Carlisle crematorium. Because the main part was undergoing building work, I had great difficulty finding where in the crematorium grounds I should be. Liz Gwyther had the same difficulty and the two of us drove round and round until we managed to find someone who gave us directions to the chapel. We got there in the nick of time quite out of breath. Susan would have found this highly amusing as, in my experience, she was rarely on time for anything.

She had specifically requested that the chaplain of the Brampton branch of the Royal British Legion should conduct the service. I am fairly confident that she would not have approved of having a lady vicar officiate. She had chosen the hymns, which were *All things bright and beautiful* and William Blake's *Jerusalem*, just what one would have expected from her. The first reflected her love of animals and the country, the second her fierce patriotism.

I think that if I had not already taken the decision to move in response to my father's request, the decision might have been made for me by Susan's death. She had been such a part of my years at Warwick Bridge that her absence was one more reason for not staying. It seemed very strange not to have the telephone ring and hear her voice at the other end, invariably breaking into a gruff laugh at the latest inanity of central government, local government or any other body in authority.

The cottage was sold in no time, as I knew would be the case. I decided to let Liz take Jemima and Eric, as I knew they would be happy with all her other geese to keep them company, while I gave the Light Sussex hens to two other friends, Cath and Martin Watson, who had previously taken some of my sheep. The paddocks seemed unbelievably quiet after the geese and hens had gone.

I brought Robbie the ram lamb away from his mother and Crosby and put him with Mr Universe. The two of them got on very well and at night would settle down together, sometimes opposite each other when it would look as if Mr Universe was imparting fatherly words of wisdom to his young son, while he had the opportunity. I wondered if he was telling him about the Highland Show and warning him to have nothing to do with it.

'If you see that woman with a halter in her hand, run like hell or you're for it,' I imagined him saying.

Robbie was promised to my friends, Marlene and Gordon Brown, who lived at Shap, where he would be kept company by another Ryeland ram lamb until I could find a new smallholding. At least in the meantime he would now be with someone of his own age.

Seven years before, I had left Newcastle and come to Cumbria with two dogs for company. I could not have imagined then all that had happened since. Nor could I have anticipated returning to the north east still with Holly and Chloe in tow, only this time accompanied by Tabitha the cat and a handful of sheep. Mr Universe, Titan, Topsy and the Ryeland ewes were all destined for temporary residence on the Gibside estate. From there, who knows which high road the Eden Flock may travel next?

AFTERWORD

This book is dedicated to the memory of my son, Stephen, and my father, Martin. I miss them both.

Two other special people who are no longer with us deserve to be commemorated. One is Susan Bull, whose constant and unswerving support during foot and mouth kept me sane. The other is Margaret Brown, who gave my sheep a second home at the end and who, sadly and unexpectedly, died just as I was leaving Cumbria to return to the north east.

My heartfelt thanks go to both of them and to so many others without whose support I might have given up my battle. Among these I would like particularly to thank:

His Royal Highness the Prince of Wales and his assistant private secretary, Elizabeth Buchanan, for their concern and interest; the Royal Agricultural Benevolent Institution and the Addington Fund for their financial assistance; the Rt Hon David Maclean MP for his tenacity; Susan Bryden and her father, Drew Taylor, from whom Mr Universe was acquired; the Press Association's Paul Watson for following my plight and Owen Humphreys for doing wonders with his camera; Dr Christina McFarlane for keeping my sheep supplied with antibiotic and me with vitamin tablets; Sandie Davison for introducing me to Pat Walker of North Yorkshire Smallholders and Pat for listening to me for hours on the telephone and always managing to give me the will to fight on; Jane Barribal of Farmtalking who worked tirelessly, manning a telephone help line for farmers during foot and mouth; Mary Critchley who wore out her laptop keeping an eye on the government and who was not afraid to say just what she thought; Peter Kindersley who made it possible for me to engage solicitors Burges Salmon and Simon Leach for all his help; Amanda Jane Ayres (whose woolly namesake went to Highgrove with Harry) and her husband Tim who both supported me in so many different ways; Ellie Logan and Pat Fisher of Save Animal Deaths for their inspiring commitment; Maggie Davies who was always on stand by in case MAFF arrived; Anne Hopper for her radio work during foot and mouth and for helping out with the tree planting and the foreword to this book; Doreen Parsons for her help over the animal health petition and the tree planting; Suzanne and Peter Greenhill, who are still working hard for the hefted flocks, for their constant encouragement; Liz Gwyther for her pictures of my sheep and her friendship; my vets at Craig Robinson, Jonathan Lomax and Julie Scarlett for all their efforts with the Eden Flock, before, during and after foot and mouth and Colin Lindsay of Capontree Vet Centre for his recent work with Mr Universe; Norman Ruddick for all his help during lambing and the hours of sitting up after my calls for help; Judy and Colin Randall for their pastoral care; Marie Kitchen who came to my aid when I needed a paddock for my sheep and cared for them so well during their time at Stony Beck; Robert Crozier for all his help and professional advice; Julian Thurgood for creating my website and making such a wonderful job of it; my son Peter who set up my computer and got me started and Denis Hitchen who has kept me right since and sorted me out so many times when I have messed up; my three transatlantic e-mail friends, Barbara Vohassek, Mary June Norman and Sandra Rudd, who have been so supportive; Charles, who supported me throughout from a distance and without whom this book would not have been written and Dawn Robertson of Hayloft for her speed and efficiency in bringing this book to publication.

As for MAFF and DEFRA, no, I am not apologising for giving you such a hard time and, yes, I do know that you refer to me as the Rottweiler. Let us just hope that the lessons learned from this crisis are taken to heart so that never again will farmers, smallholders and everyone else living and working in the countryside have to face the sights, hear the sounds or bear the sadness and suffering that spread through Cumbria during 2001.

Last, but by no means least, my prize ram, Mr Universe who, despite all he has had to put up with, has remained as placid as ever and is still partial to a digestive biscuit... and a cuddle.

Changing the Face of Carlisle, The Life and Times of Percy Dalton, City Engineer and Surveyor, 1926-1949, Marie K. Dickens
(£8, ISBN 095 407 1190)

From Clogs and Wellies to Shiny Shoes, A Windermere Lad s Memories of South Lakeland, Miles R. M. Bolton (£12.50, ISBN 190 452 4028)

A History of Kaber, Helen McDonald and Christine Dowson,
(£8, ISBN 095 407 1166)

Gone to Blazes, Life as a Cumbrian Fireman, David Stubbings
(£9.95, ISBN 095 407 114X)

Changing Times, A History of Bolton, Barbara Cotton
(£12.50, ISBN 095 407 1131)

Better by Far a Cumberland Hussar, A History of the Westmorland and Cumberland Yeomanry, Colin Bardgett
(Hardback, £26.95, ISBN 0954071123/ Paperback, £16.95, ISBN 0954071115)

Northern Warrior, the Story of Sir Andreas de Harcla, Adrian Rogan
(£8.95, ISBN 095 232 8283)

A Riot of Thorn & Leaf, Dulcie Matthews (£7.95, ISBN 095 407 1107)

Riding the Stang, Dawn Robertson (£9.99, ISBN 095 232 8224)

Secrets and Legends of Old Westmorland, Peter Koronka & Dawn Robertson
(Hardback, £17.95, ISBN 0952328240/Paperback, £11.95, ISBN 0952328291)

The Irish Influence, Migrant Workers in Northern England,
Harold Slight (£4.95, 095 232 8259)

North Country Tapestry, Sylvia Mary McCosh (£10, 095 186 9000)

Between Two Gardens, The Diary of two Border Gardens,
Sylvia Mary McCosh (£5.95, 090 081 117X)

Dacre Castle, A short history of the Castle and the Dacre Family,
E. H. A. Stretton (£5.50, 095 186 9019)

Little Ireland, Memories of a Cleator Moor Childhood, Sean Close
(£7.95, ISBN 095 4067 304)

A Slip from Grace, More tales from Little Ireland, Sean Close
(£10.00, ISBN 095 4067 312)

You can order any of our books by writing to:
Hayloft Publishing Ltd., South Stainmore, Kirkby Stephen,
Cumbria, CA17 4EU, UK.
Please enclose a cheque plus £2 for UK postage and packing.
or telephone: +44 (0)17683) 42300
For more information see: www.hayloft.org.uk